Putting
wrong
things
right:

Environmental Health from **1952** to **2012**

Edited by William Hatchett

"We entered the profession at the sharp end ... we did anything and everything, at times dirty, smelly, dangerous and frustrating but our job of 'putting wrong things right' was surely one of the best and all for £360 a year plus £30 London weighting. We were there!"

Eric Silvester 1916-2012

Putting wrong things right: Environmental Health from 1952 to 2012

Edited by William Hatchett

Designed by Jon Heal

CIEH

First published 2014 by CIEH

The moral rights of the authors have been asserted in accordance with the Copyright, Design and Patent Act 1988

British Library Cataloguing in Publication Data. A catalogue record for this book is available from the British Library.

ISBN 978-1-906989-67-5

Printed and bound by Hobbs the Printers Ltd

Contents

Advertisement in *The Sanitarian*, 1955

Acknowledgements

The most significant recent historian of the Chartered Institute of Environmental Health was a remarkable man who served as its general secretary for a quarter of a century, from 1950 to 1977, Reginald Johnson MBE. The professional body celebrated its centenary in 1983 and to commemorate this event Mr Johnson, who had been a well-regarded sanitary inspector, wrote a volume entitled *A Century of Progress: The History of the Institution of Environmental Health Officers 1883-1983*. The editor of this work has drawn heavily on that blue paperback in compiling this account.

In 2009, two distinguished figures from the profession, both former presidents, Andrew Banfield and John Tiffney, researched an update to Mr Johnson's book, telling the story of the next 25 years. Both had been heavily involved in the growth and successes of the CIEH and in its governance. They were helped in tracking down facts and documents by Tina Garrity, the CIEH's information and communications manager, and Graham Jukes, the current chief executive, who provided editorial and factual support.

The Diamond Jubilee of Her Majesty Queen Elizabeth II's reign, in 2012, was a significant milestone in the life of the CIEH. To mark the Jubilee year, Graham wrote to retired members of the CIEH, asking if they would like to contribute memories and old photographs, recording their memories over the Queen's reign.

Their vivid contributions were incorporated in a souvenir issue of *Environmental Health News*, published in June 2012. It was Graham's idea to combine this treasure trove of material with the manuscript earlier produced by Mr Banfield and Mr Tiffney in order to compile this book and I was privileged to be asked to carry out the task. My researches also led me to the CIEH's fascinating library, poring over leather-bound journals and long-forgotten reference books on topics as diverse as drains, bed-sit housing and tropical diseases. This unique corpus of learning forms the recent history, in printed form, of environmental health.

During the editing of this book, I received the sad news that one of the most tireless and inspiring of the old sanitary inspectors, Eric Silvester, had died. Through his spidery, hand-written notes, Eric had been a constant commentator throughout my 15 years as editor of *EHN*; his uplifting words, in a final contribution, gave the book its title.

William Hatchett, Editor, *Environmental Health News*

William Hatchett worked on Community Care *and* Housing *magazines before his current job. He was named housing journalist of the year in 1998 and PPA independent publishers' editor of the year in 2013 and has written for many national publications including* The Guardian, The Observer *and* New Statesman. *He lives in London.*

Contributors

Our thanks to the retired, student and current members, and others, whose generous contributions of reminiscences and photographs have made this book possible: Rupert Adams, Lisa Ackerley, Diana Adamson, Mick Aldridge, Chris Allen, Peter Archer, Julia Atkins, Jon Averns, Andrew Banfield, Stephen Battersby, David Beardmore, JL Billings, Wayne Blything, BS Boulter, Graham Butterworth, Raymond Cannon, Andrew Charnick, Ron Charnick, David Clapham, Ron Coebe, Chris Cornish, AS Crowe, Maurice Duffield, Rodney Dykes, Alan Eames, David England, Jack Fish, Brian Fox, Leonard Griffiths, James Goss, Peter Hacker, Brian Hanna, Wilson Hargreaves, Kate Harris, Arthur Harrison, George Hart, Roger Hart, Warren Haynes, Alan Higgins, Ewan Holt, Norman Jackson, Maldwyn Jones, Maurice Jones, Mike Jacob, Norman Jackson, Lynda John, Graham Jukes, Roy Kaye, Ned Kingcott, DR Krieger, Alan Lacey, Rodney Lamb, Adeline K Lewis, Tony Lewis, Geoffrey Lindsey, Adrian Lord, Ian MacArthur, Kenneth Mahers, FD Marriott, John Marsh, Brian Mayers, Gary McGrogan, Douglas McMurray, George Mills, Julie Monk, Gareth Moore, Jenny Morris, Robert Morton, Gary Moyes, Don Oliver, Terry Oliver, PC Oxley, Geoffrey Podger, Howard Price, David Purchon, R Redgate, Janet Russell, Neil Scott, Alan Shankster, Eric Silvester, Graham H Smith, Andy Statham, David Statham, Alan Summerfield, Joanna Tawel, Yunes Teinaz, John Tiffney, Alastair Tomlinson, Geoff Ward, David J Wells, C Wilks and Nick Wilson.

Advertisement in *The Sanitarian*, 1955

Photographs

INSIDE COVER
Charles Hewitt/Getty

THE NEW ELIZABETHANS
p12-13: SSPL via Getty Images, p14: AFP/Getty, p17: Popperfoto/Getty, p20: Raymond Kleboe/Getty,
p22: Bert Hardy/Getty, p24: George Hart, p26: Terry Fincher/Getty, p29: Thurston Hopkins/Picture Post/Getty,
p31: Monty Fresco/Getty, p33: Arthur Harrison, p36: Topical Press Agency/Getty

WHITE HEAT
p42-43: Reg Speller/Getty, p45: Bentley Arcives/Popperfoto/Getty, p47: Harry Todd/Getty,
p54: Bert Hardy Advertising Archive/Getty, p56: PC Oxley, p58: Arthur Harrison, p60: Rolls Press/Getty,
p62: Wikimedia Commons/C Wippet, Wikimedia Commons/Allan Warren (2),
Wikimedia Commons/Graeme Mclean, Cattani/Getty

THE PARTY'S OVER
p64-65: Ken Goff/Time & Life Pictures/Getty, p66: Wikimedia Commons/Malcolm Campbell,
p69: Graham Turner/Getty, p72: Andy Statham, p77: The Image Bank/Getty, p78: The Image Bank/Getty,
p81: John Bulmer/Getty, p84: Kevin Holt/Associated Newspapers/Rex, Keystone/Getty,
p85: Hulton Archive/Archive, Michael Fresco/Getty, Hulton Archive

STORMS AND MARKETS
p86-87: David Levenson/Getty, p89: AFP/Getty, p93: Express/Getty, p95: UIG via Getty Images,
p99: Ron Charnick, p107: Wikimedia Commons/Christopher Newbury

A SHRINKING WORLD
p108-109: Sven Crutzmann/Mambo/Getty, p113: Daniel Garcia/AFP/Getty, p120: geogphotos/Alamy,
p123: Joel Robine/AFP/Getty, p130: John Sturrock/Alamy

THE RETURN OF PUBLIC HEALTH
p132-133: Alexis Maryon, p135: Johnny Eggit/Getty, p139: Alexis Maryon, p142: Matt Cardy/Getty,
p144: Peter Macdiarmid/Getty, p149: Diverse Images/Getty, p155: Oli Scarff/Getty,
p157: Daniel Berehulak/Getty, p159: Diverse Images/UIG/Getty,
p162: Wikimedia Commons/The Machine Stops

Foreword

Several histories of Britain since the Second World War have appeared recently, some focusing on the politics of the period, some on its social history. But few have captured the nitty gritty of the changing world around us so well as this history of public and environmental health over the past 60 years.

Sometimes when those of us who are old now look back on our childhoods in the 1940s and 1950s we can be tempted to romanticise the daily experiences of those times. The London smog had a certain Dickensian glamour as one struggled home with a muffler round the face. We remember or heard tell of the strong community spirit of the slums. We were too glad to be able to get our rationed food supplies at all to worry too much about their quality or provenance. Somehow in spite of the hardships and deprivations we may fondly imagine now as we look back that we were 'all in it together', and that those years were the best of times as well as the worst.

This volume is a great corrective. Those bad conditions of the 1940s were a national disgrace. They were big wrongs and they caused death and ill-health on a major scale. They were aspects of the five 'Giant Evils' in society identified by William Beveridge in his great 1943 report: squalor, ignorance, want, idleness and disease. They needed to be dealt with.

Many writers have written about Beveridge and Bevan, and the creation of the welfare state and the National Health Service. Much less attention is usually paid to the footsoldiers in the frontline of improving public and environmental health: those who gradually spread the network of smokeless zones to implement the Clean Air Act, those who identified and cleared the slums, those who inspected the farms and abattoirs, the food shops and restaurants and forced the elimination of dirt, infestations and infection from the food chain and those who cleared up many other sources of squalor and disease.

Here in this volume these unsung heroes, the environmental health officers, are properly remembered and appreciated – often in their own words and with their own vivid and graphic memories of incidents and individuals involved in the struggle. They have never been romantic figures, never much in the public eye – but they have always been the best of resolute and determined professional officers, identifying wrongs and putting them right steadily and steadfastly, one after another, year in year out.

They and their work are one of the reasons why the Britain of 2014 is so obviously a better and healthier place than it was in the struggling 1940s. But their work is by no means over yet. For, as this book so well reveals, no sooner is one environmental health challenge mastered but another seems to loom up, needing new knowledge to analyse, new solutions to resolve and new skills of persuasion and determination in the front-line environmental health professionals to drive home. Long may the profession flourish to give society this essential protection.

Derek Osborn

Derek Osborn CB is a vice president of the Chartered Institute of Environmental Health, and was a member of the CIEH's environmental health commission, which published Agendas for Change *in 1997. He was director general of environmental protection in the Department of the Environment from 1990 to 1996, chairman of the European Environment Agency from 1995 to 2000, president of the National Society for Clean Air in 1999, president of the EU's Sustainable Development Observatory from 2006 to 2008 and is currently president of Stakeholder Forum for Our Common Future.*

Introduction

The main inspiration for this book was a treasured family volume entitled *Sixty Years a Queen*. The lavishly illustrated publication with its gilt-embossed frontispiece was published in 1897 to celebrate the 60-year-reign of Queen Victoria. It is an evocative record of the domestic and international achievements of the period in which Britain became a modern industrial economy and rose to global dominance.

Jubilees are both national and personal milestones – they are a time to take stock and to evaluate what we have achieved. As the Diamond Jubilee of Her Majesty Queen Elizabeth II in 2012 came into view, I had an idea. It was to assemble a history of the environmental health profession from 1952 to 2012, told mainly through the first-hand accounts of practitioners.

With such a book in mind, in 2011, I wrote to all retired CIEH members asking for personal reflections on their work in environmental health over the past six decades. I was inundated with contributions and a selection was published in *Environmental Health News* in June 2012, to coincide with the Jubilee celebrations.

In order to produce *Putting wrong things right*, these rich reminiscences were combined with the historical researches of past CIEH presidents Andrew Banfield and John Tiffney and a collection of memories produced by retired CIEH member and ex-national serviceman Barrie Sheard. They were then augmented by more recent reminiscences, collected by *EHN* editor William Hatchett. *EHN* art editor, Jon Heal, designed the book. It was hard work but a labour of love.

What began as a tribute to Her Majesty has evolved into a unique record of the often unseen and uncelebrated history of a chartered profession the members of which have done so much to improve the health of people and communities. To read their recollections is a privilege. I am immensely pleased that, in documenting 60 years of environmental health, we have been able to capture the memories of the first generation of post-war health inspectors who achieved so much, while they can still tell their stories.

I was born in 1952 as Her Majesty began her reign. I may not have known it as a child, but throughout my life, like all of Her Majesty's subjects, I have been protected by improvements delivered by the environmental health profession. I can clearly remember walking to school in the 1950s and 1960s in the dense smogs of a London winter and experiencing at home the benefits of the rolling programme of conversion to smokeless fuel. I came into the profession in the early-1970s during the last phase of slum clearance in London and can still remember my student experiences of inspecting post-war prefabs and terraced houses. Whilst occupied, they were certainly unfit for occupation (although, on reflection, they were probably far better than the current 'beds in sheds'). Those who had gone before me had left an indelible impression. Through slum clearance schemes and by enforcing the Clean Air Act of 1956, they had laid the groundwork for a better Britain.

The outcome of the profession's work is tangible and can be measured in improvements to quality of life. During the past 60 years we, as a profession, have been at the forefront of providing improvements in housing, food and drink, workplace safety, pest control, air quality, waste management, drainage and nuisances prejudicial to health. Life expectancy has increased for men by 11 years and for women by 13 years, not just through medical intervention (although this has played a significant part) but by addressing the causes of of ill-health.

This book also illustrates how, in the post-war decades, a profession that had emerged during Britain's industrial revolution became more and more outward-facing. In the 1990s, the knowledge base of environmental health was found to have great relevance to the global concerns brought into focus by the Rio Earth Summit in 1992. It was also the decade when the Iron Curtain came down. The CIEH's input was sought by the World Health Organisation and the European Commission, for example in programmes to improve the degraded environments and underdeveloped infrastructures of Eastern and Central Europe.

I was honoured to be closely involved with this work as an advisor and consultant to the WHO supporting the introduction of environmental health solutions to countries in political transition, particularly working with my friend, the inspiring advisor on environment and health to the WHO's European region, Xavier Bonnefoy.

Some things have changed. Whilst food may be cheaper and more plentiful and varied than it was in the 1950s, its calorific value and sugar, salt and saturated fat content have become matters of great concern. Addressing 'lifestyle issues' (the term would not have been recognised in the 1950s) is an important aspect of health improvement. Local authorities recycled then (it was called 'salvage') but not to the extent that they do now. Today's concerns about reducing energy use and lowering carbon emissions would have seemed incongruous when Queen Elizabeth began her reign and politicians had a simple imperative to increase industrial output.

Other environmental health issues have come full circle. In recent years, housing has been neglected as a national priority, to the point that the condition of our housing stock has become a pressing challenge once more for the environmental health profession. We are also experiencing widening differences in life expectancy and quality of life between communities and regions and growing health inequalities. In an era in which 'deregulation' risks diminishing long-fought for protections of the nation's safety and wellbeing, the CIEH is just as relevant and needed today as it was in 1952. As we approach the next election, the CIEH will be lobbying all parties and attempting to influence their manifestos in order to re-address environmental health issues as a priority.

This book illustrates, from first-hand accounts, how the CIEH, from being a relatively small membership organisation has evolved into a Royal chartered professional body with more than 120 staff, at the centre of a public health social enterprise with a world-wide reach. We are public-facing and fully-engaged in the key debates of our time, providing a positive influence on national and international health improvement agendas.

I would like to pay tribute to my predecessors and colleagues who have worked so diligently to improve public health over the past 60 years, some of whose voices are heard in the following pages. We have only scratched the surface of the work done by the whole of the profession but these recollections provide a first-hand record of many of the challenges they faced, some humorous, some perilous, certainly necessary and always for the public good. My personal thanks go to all those whose contributions have made this book possible. Those who work in environmental health should be extremely proud of the contribution they have made. Long may the profession flourish and maintain its motto *amicus humani generis*, which translates as 'friend of the human race'.

Graham M Jukes OBE, CFCIEH, chief executive, CIEH

Graham Jukes began his local government career in environmental health in 1971. After leaving local government as assistant chief EHO in a London borough he was appointed under secretary at the CIEH in 1988. In that and subsequent roles he took responsibility for all legal, technical, policy and educational matters and leading the CIEH's response to European and UK legislation underpinning modern environmental health practice. He was appointed CIEH chief executive in January 2000. Over a career spanning 43 years, he has held a number of elected and volunteer positions within the environmental health community. He has been an advisor to the World Health Organisation and UK government departments and committees on environmental health and sustainable development policy and practice. He is company secretary to the International Federation of Environmental Health, holds a number of trustee and environmental health-connected executive and non-executive directorships and is chair of governors of his local school. He was elected a fellow of the CIEH in 1990, a fellow of the Faculty of Public Health in 2004 and was recognised by Her Majesty in the New Year's Honours List of 2014 with the award of an OBE for his services to environmental health in the UK and abroad.

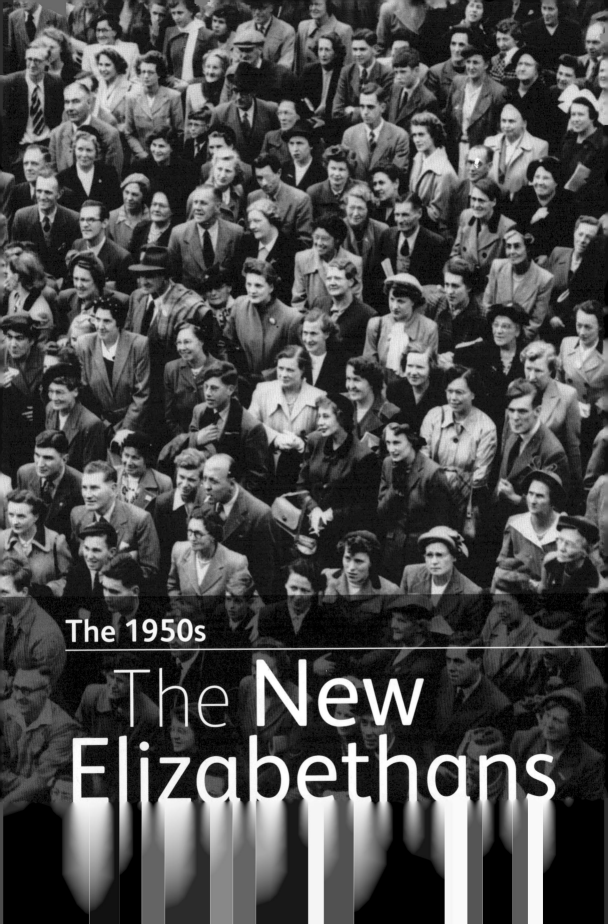

The 1950s

The New Elizabethans

On a cold February day in 1952, Queen Elizabeth II touched down in a British Overseas Airways Corporation airliner at London's new airport, Heathrow. The mood of the waiting crowd must have been sombre. Her father, George VI, had died the day before and she had been recalled from Kenya, where she was on a visit with her husband, Prince Philip.

She had not taken mourning clothes on the trip, so a set was conveyed to the aircraft, allowing her to change into appropriate attire. Wearing a black coat, hat and gloves, the Queen stood to be photographed in the cabin doorway. Only a week before, a more cheerful crowd had waved her on her way at the beginning of the trip. The King, looking frail, had made his first public appearance since the previous September.

The 26-year-old queen must have looked out over the runway at the darkly-clad crowds and felt a weight of responsibility descend on her shoulders. She did not speak and no newsreel camera captured the event. Waiting to greet her at the foot of the steps were the most important men in her kingdom – the current and previous Prime Ministers, Winston Churchill and Clement Attlee, the Deputy Prime Minister, Anthony Eden, and the Head of the Privy Council, Baron Woolton, inventor of the wartime 'Woolton pie'. They must have expressed their condolences, as camera bulbs flashed. Flags were at half-mast that day,

Queen Elizabeth II is greeted at Heathrow in February 1952, on her return from Kenya

cinemas and theatres were closed and all sports fixtures were cancelled. Slowly, the Queen and her retinue walked to the black cars that would take them to the palace. The new Elizabethan era had begun.

The beginning of the Queen's reign is often depicted as a bleak time. It is true that meat rationing did not end until 1954, that memories of the war were still vivid and that a generation of children grew up playing on bombsites. But we should not see the 1950s purely in black and white.

Three aspects of social policy impacted upon the nation's health on an unprecedented scale. Firstly, the National Health Service and the welfare state had laid to rest the ghosts of the poorhouse and the hated 1930s-style 'means test'. The NHS and the new benefit system were creations of the 1945 Labour government, based on a template provided by a Liberal, William Beveridge, whose 1942 report was an instant bestseller. The Butler Education Act of 1944 was the product of a Conservative politician, RA Butler. Although it introduced testing and selection for 11-year-olds, its mandating of universal, free secondary education gave a boost to social mobility. Lastly, council housing, advocated by both Labour and Conservative politicians and built in large numbers throughout the decade, provided new amenities and an escape route from overcrowding for millions.

Politically, the 1950s was a blue decade. After the brief post-war spell of a reforming Labour government, the Conservatives returned to power in 1951 with an elderly Winston Churchill at the helm. They were to remain in power for 13 years, the Labour party split between its left and right factions, led by Anuerin Bevan and Hugh Gaitskell respectively. The Conservatives were buoyed throughout the 1950s by economic success. Did not Prime Minister Harold Macmillan say in 1957, "most of our people have never had it so good"? Growing affluence manifested in soaring demand for cars, refrigerators and washing machines.

By the end of the decade, the first motorways would arrive, easing congestion from country lanes and holiday-thronged A-roads. There was commercial television to challenge the monopoly of the BBC – the television had replaced the wireless as the most important medium for news and entertainment. And there were supermarkets. In 1947, there were only 10 self-service stores in the UK. But after Premier supermarkets opened its first branch in Streatham in 1951 – what a novelty it must have seemed – the floodgates opened.

In the technological realm, it was the decade of the sleek jetliner and of Sputnik. Newspapers celebrated the derring-do of test pilots breaking the sound barrier – one of the icons of the decade was a hero from the *Eagle* comic, Dan Dare, pilot of the future. On the streets, young people had sufficient time and disposable income to frequent the new coffee or milk bars and to display forms of youth culture that were strident and garish enough to shock their parents. From 1953, the term 'Teddy Boy' entered the national vocabulary. Continental colour and style were appearing on the high street and in the home. In 1951, the Festival of Britain had provided a preview of things to come, showcasing the latest trends in design.

Even the national palate was evolving. In 1958, WE Cooke, chief public health inspector for Bingley in West Yorkshire, writes in *The Sanitarian,* the monthly journal of the Association of Public Health Inspectors, on the state of food. He notes: "Rationing, shortages and general dreariness of food are now things of the past. Not only have we unrestricted supplies from the sunnier climes of the Commonwealth and Europe, but home-produced food in abundant supply."

Mr Cooke enthuses about continental holidays, mass-produced meals, espresso bars and the new, gleaming self-service store or supermarket, with its stress on hygienic packaging and wrapping. He observes: "The use of Perspex and polythene containers has great possibilities and refrigerated display cabinets have greatly extended the range of perishable goods which can be sold." Salmonella, Cooke notes, causes 44 per cent of food poisoning outbreaks, with infected meat the main cause.

The Food and Drugs Act of 1955 changed the working life of many inspectors. Almost as important for the decade as housing and clean air legislation, it significantly toughened rules on food safety and hygiene and greatly increased the numbers of premises to be inspected. Jack Love recalls a comment made on the act by a prominent member of the association, Morley Parry: "I don't care how many in-depth inspections you carry out, as long as they are damned good ones."

Mr Cooke writes in his 1958 article that the legislation has been patchily applied. He tells the sad tale of a family in Rugby poisoned by their under-cooked Christmas turkey in 1957 and calls for more to be done to educate housewives about temperature control.

If Elizabeth's long reign officially began on the death of her father in 1952, it gained its official confirmation on Coronation Day, 2 June 1953. There would be other royal landmarks over the coming decades – the Queen's Silver Jubilee in 1977, the royal wedding of Charles and Diana in 1981 and her Diamond Jubilee in 2012, coinciding with London's hosting of the Olympic and Paralympic Games. All were marked by national celebrations and street parties. But the Coronation was special. After a dreadful war, the UK was beginning a fresh chapter with a young monarch. Technology seemed to offer infinite possibilities and there was a promise of increased social mobility, removing the last vestiges of Edwardian 'Upstairs Downstairs' Britain.

This coronation was the first to be televised. More than 20 million Britons watched the event, reverentially narrated by Richard Dimbleby, through this still-novel medium. Many were experiencing the 'goggle box' for the first time. Sets with tiny screens encased in large wooden cabinets cost about £85 (the average income was £12 a week). The welcome news that a Briton, Edmund Hillary, and Sherpa Tenzing had conquered Mount Everest had come the day before.

The Sanitarian may hitherto have been silent on the fact of a new monarch but it made up for this reticence in its June 1953 edition. Its editorial announcement is an expression of hope for the new Elizabethan era: "We wish Her Majesty a long and happy and above all, a peaceful reign. Under her rule may the country and the whole Commonwealth and Empire prosper and flourish. During her reign may she witness the establishment of mutual confidence and respect between all the countries of the world so that, freed of the threat of war, their peoples may be free to devote the whole of their energies to improve the standard of life and to living a better and fuller existence."

Returning swiftly to everyday life, the issue then turns its attention to dwelling houses, blowflies and canal boats.

Tin baths filled with hot water from the kettle or boiler were commonly used in the 1950s

Professional issues

The technological and social advances of the 1950s were mirrored in the evolving functions, training and governance of local authority sanitary inspectors. Over the course of the decade, they would gain a new job title and an improved system of professional qualification, appropriate for the new era.

Their job, which had evolved from that of the inspector of nuisance in the 19th century, was to safeguard the public against contaminated food and harm or injury from the workplace and the environment. Following a template set by the 1848 Public Health Act, inspectors worked 'under the general direction' of medical officers of health – officials with medical qualifications who ran councils' often extensive sanitary or public health departments (see 'The local authority' below).

In November 1952, the Sanitary Inspectors' Association's new president, Lord Milner, writes in the association's monthly journal, *The Sanitarian*. He lists inspectors' duties. It is a formidable catalogue, each topic associated with Acts of Parliament and detailed regulations: 'Atmospheric pollution, working conditions in factories, offices and shops, drainage and sewage disposal, nuisances, offensive trades, infectious diseases, housing in the widest sense, covering general repairs, slum clearance and re-development, overcrowding and rent restriction, food hygiene, catering establishments, meat and food inspection, slaughterhouses, dairies and what is known as health education.'

Each year, every medical officer of health compiled a detailed report on the work of his department (they were nearly all men) and the state of health in his locality, noting mortality trends and any particularly significant disease outbreaks. Long before quangos and micro-management from oversized Whitehall departments, councils were enormously important in the daily life and health of their citizens. There were still slums; rag and bone men plied the streets with horses and carts and 'offensive trades' connected with manufacturing, slaughtering and rendering went on virtually under people's noses.

It took a long time for the fruits of post-war prosperity to reach every corner. Mick Aldridge, a retired public health inspector, recalls typical living conditions in the early 1950s: "The majority of [people] had no running water except one tap and then only when the boiler in the kitchen or scullery was alight. The toilet was outside. At best, it was a WC, at worst a 'midden' serving a number of families… a midden was a pan or just a hole in the ground covered by a wooden seat. It discharged into the ground and occasionally a shovel of earth or ash was put into the hole. Some councils ran a service to dig out the contents… There were often no fixed baths. Most who are over 60 will recall the tin bath that hung on the wall being brought down and filled for the weekly ablutions. It was a bit cold by the time the last family member got in."

In the 1950s, clean water supplies meant that outbreaks of cholera had been eliminated and that typhoid was extremely uncommon. Tuberculosis had been the major premature killer of the poor since the 19th century, causing more deaths than all other diseases put together. Now, thanks to antibiotics, the BCG vaccine and the mandatory adoption of milk pasteurisation and TB-testing for cattle, it was in retreat but it still aroused fear, especially for the young.

Similarly, vaccination had greatly reduced deaths caused by the 'childhood diseases' scarlet fever, diphtheria, whooping cough and measles, but they lingered, evoking the spectre of the 'sick room'. For Roger Hart, it was contracting such an illness that governed his eventual career choice. He writes: "I was only nine at the time of Her Majesty's accession in 1952. In 1951, I had contracted scarlet fever, which was common then and could be quite serious. To my mother's relief, I started to recover, but recovery brought a shock. My room was to be fumigated with everything in it, including my treasured teddy. On the appointed day, two men, in navy overalls, arrived in a navy blue van, with a heraldic crest on the side. They did their dastardly deed and I returned to my room. Teddy was still there and apparently unharmed!"

After the incident, Mr Hart passed his '11 plus' and went to grammar school. He had intended to be a woodwork teacher, but put a chisel through his hand and spent his 17th birthday in hospital. Change of plan – he applied to the local council's public health department to work as an administrator. He recalls: "The interview made no mention of attending college one day a week and getting qualifications. I was appointed on the princely sum of £32 a month. I still have the pay slip. It was a small fortune to me.

"The practical work was very enjoyable. It brought me into contact with those navy blue vans, with crests on the side. I could never have realised at nine that I would eventually come to manage the fumigation service, along with pest control, drain-clearing and the cleansing of verminous people. I managed that service for 10 years then became the manager of the public mortuary – one of the best jobs in local government, as I never had a customer complaint! Satisfyingly, in all the years during which I managed the service, we never disinfected a house for scarlet fever – progress in public health. After my local government years, I became a consultant and travelled the world. God bless the Queen."

Extremely contagious and potentially deadly, smallpox was a 19th-century horror that also persisted. There were sporadic UK outbreaks throughout the 20th century: it struck Brighton in 1950 and Britain's last outbreaks were in 1962 in Bradford and South Wales, where 19 people died. Polio, a highly infectious viral disease, was late to attract an effective vaccine. It, too, persisted in the UK in the 1950s.

Causing concern, deaths from cancers were rising. An editorial in *The Sanitarian* of June 1953 records an astonishing increase in the death rate for lung cancer for males, from 85 per million in 1931 to 530 per million in 1951. Today, we know why: in the early 1950s, 80 per cent of British adults smoked. The 1953 article gives no hint of a link between lung cancer and tobacco, but it states: "Cancer is replacing tuberculosis as a public health problem, but further research into the causative factors is urgently necessary."

The professional body

The Sanitary Inspectors' Association had 4,549 members in 1952 when Elizabeth came to the throne, the vast majority working for councils in England and Wales. Members' annual subscription was £2 12s 6d. Local branches, including a sea and airport branch, held training and social events. The branches were aggregated into 14 centres, which elected representatives to the association's governing body, its General Council.

Reginald Johnson MBE, general secretary in 1952

Since 1937, the association's administrative and executive base had been a modest set of rooms over a bank, at 19 Grosvenor Place in Westminster. Here, Reginald Johnson MBE, who was appointed in 1950 and held the post until his retirement in 1977, served as general secretary, the association's senior paid official. Before that, he had worked in local government in Enfield, Coventry, Watford and finally Walsall, as deputy chief public health inspector. From 1955 when he joined the World Health Organisation's expert panel on environmental health, he served on WHO technical committees. He also sat on the UK's Meat Hygiene Group and was secretary for two years of the Ice Cream Alliance (contaminated ice cream had concerned inspectors since the 19th century).

Mr Johnson was initially the only technical officer at the association's HQ. He was later joined by an assistant secretary (technical) and a public relations officer. Among his many roles was the editorship of *The Sanitarian*. It is Mr Johnson who provides us with the best account of the association's eventful journey through the 1950s in an official history, published in 1983: *A Century of Progress*.

The government was now allocating significant resources to post-war reconstruction. In 1951, a new Ministry of Local Government and Planning took over responsibility for planning and housing from the health ministry, placing them firmly in the area of local government. Labour's Hugh Dalton now masterminded a vigorous house-building programme. He was quite critical of Aneurin Bevan's previous efforts (Mr Bevan had run the housing programme as health minister). The crusade to build was continued by the Conservatives, when they won the election of October 1951 and appointed Harold Macmillan as housing minister.

A mandate was being delivered to Grosvenor Place, from the association's General Council, to improve and modernise. In 1952, the association's Defence League (a fund to covers members' legal costs) was wound up. A new body, the Sanitary Officers Guild, came into being as a trade union. This allowed the association to refocus as a professional body.

Dr Charles Hill, the 'radio doctor', spoke at the 1952 conference

As recorded in *The Sanitarian* with black and white photographs, the association's 59th annual conference in Brighton in 1952 was a buoyant affair. A daily programme of speeches and technical presentations was interspersed by visits to the Shippams Paste Factory, a farm, a fruit orchard and packing station and a sewage-works. As well as the formal dinner and dance, side events included a whist drive, instructional films and 'American-style' square dancing.

Guest of honour that year was a national celebrity: Dr Charles Hill, parliamentary secretary to the Ministry of Food. Dr Hill had gained the nickname 'the radio doctor' during the war and was later to serve as a Conservative housing minister. In his presentation on the Food and Drugs Act of 1938, he flattered and amused delegates telling them: "You suffer from the fact that so much of your work is unknown and dramatic but absolutely vital. I wish to see the development of your role in future years as friendly advisors."

In 1953, the association's members balloted to scrap their now old-fashioned sounding job title. It took a further four years and a private members' bill for their wish to be granted, but in 1957, they were re-christened public health inspectors. Their professional body duly became the Association of Public Health Inspectors and gained a new coat of arms. It was decided that the coat of arms should incorporate the association's long-standing emblem, a five-pointed star or pentacle – a symbol associated with the Greek goddess of health, Hygeia. The association's motto was also retained – 'amicus humani generis' meaning 'friend of the human race'. The association's journal, *The Sanitarian*, did not reflect the change of name until 1964, when it became *The Public Health Inspector*.

In parallel, a thoroughgoing look at qualification and training was going on. A Ministry of Health working party was set up in 1951 and published a substantial report in August 1953. One of its members was Ronald Williams, Coventry's popular chief sanitary inspector. The working party's report led, in 1957, to a new examining body, the Public Health Inspectors Education Board, combining representatives from the association, local authorities, the Royal Sanitary Institute and the professional bodies for veterinary surgeons and municipal engineers. APHI held almost half of the places on the new board, as opposed to only two out of the 30 places on its predecessor. The existing basic examination, augmented by 'tickets' in meat and smoke inspection administered by the Royal Sanitary Institute, was to be replaced by a new diploma, involving pupillage with a local authority.

It took a long time for the details to be agreed by the various local authority associations and the first diploma examinations were not held until 1964. Of the 144 candidates, 129 passed, "providing convincing proof of the high standard of training which the diploma scheme provided," Mr Johnson notes in *A Century of Progress*. The same year, the association's first gold, silver and bronze Ronald Williams Awards were presented to outstanding students.

The association's membership increased throughout the 1950s, as did the size of its annual conference. Mr Johnson records with modest pride that an exhibition of commercial goods and services was added for the first time to the Margate conference of 1959. The number of delegates at Scarborough in 1960 reached 2,000, also for the first time.

The local authority

Camberwell Borough Council was a typical London local authority before the 1965 re-organisation in the capital, when it was absorbed into Southwark. The council had begun as one of 28 metropolitan borough councils created by the London Government Act of 1899. The fourth largest, it was made up of the former villages and manors of Camberwell and Peckham and the hamlets of Nunhead and Dulwich. Camberwell town hall was located in Peckham Road.

The council had 60 councillors – three per ward – and 10 aldermen. Councillors held office for three years, the aldermen they appointed served for six years, half of them retiring every third year. The council's standing committees were: establishment, finance, housing management, libraries and art gallery, planning and development, public health and public services and works (roads maintenance, parks, surveying, cleansing and road safety). Each member of the council served on at least two committees.

Hanging out the washing, dried by hand in a mangle, in a south London back yard

The town clerk was the chief administrative officer of the council. His department was responsible for legal matters, bills, baths, cemeteries, crematoria, press and public relations, entertainments and road safety. In all, there were 1,900 council staff.

The council had an annual rate revenue of £2m but a debt of £13m against assets of £17m (mainly housing), largely because of its extensive inter-war housing programme. In 1939, there were 40,000 dwellings in the borough. However, at the end of World War Two, only 400 were undamaged by air attacks.

There were approximately 5,000 dwellings in council ownership in the late-1950s. Sceaux Gardens (affected by a tragic fatal fire in 2009) was the largest, most up-to-date estate in the borough, with the tallest buildings.

Blocks of council flats were designed by the borough architect for the director of housing and were built up to a height of 17 storeys. They were allocated using a points system based on need. The council's direct labour force constructed a quarter of the homes. Housing made up well over 90 per cent of the council's £2.3m annual capital programme.

The public health department was run by a medical officer of health, the post having been created in 1856, just after the borough arms were granted to Camberwell vestry, the parish authority. The department was concerned with the control of infectious diseases, the inspection of sanitary arrangements, standards of food and hygiene in shops, restaurants and factories and public health education.

Staff inspected drains, ordered the internal and external improvement of buildings, served nuisance notices under by-laws and acts of Parliament, destroyed pests, seized unsound food and disinfected bedding and household items. There was also a civil defence department, half of the staff of which were women.

Chief medical officers were to be moved to health authorities by the Social Services Act of 1970, which set up new social services departments in councils.

The workplace

The war was a recent event in the 1950s and it was a decade of conflicts involving Britain, for example in Korea, Kenya, Egypt and Malaysia. Many inspectors, working for urban and rural districts and county and municipal boroughs, had direct personal experience of the armed services, whether as regulars, on national service or working alongside former services personnel.

Peter Hacker writes: "On Coronation Day 1953, I was in the hold of a troop ship humping kit bags prior to landing next day at Port Said. Ahead was 18 months' national service in the canal zone. The Coronation was broadcast over the ship's tannoy and I felt so homesick… The Armed Services knew exactly what to do with sanitary inspectors or, in those days, hygiene assistants in the Royal Army Medical Corps. It was inevitable to have a foreign posting. I was up and down the canal zone but nine months with the British Military Mission in Aqaba, at the northern tip of the Red Sea, as a staff sergeant was a good experience.

"In public health, the immediate post-war years had seen the arrival of residual pesticides which had revolutionised the battle against insect vermin. In my own authority, all new council houses were sprayed with a ribbon of insecticide (Gammexane) around all skirting boards and architraves to prevent incoming occupants infesting the house, especially with bed bugs (the bane of our lives). It was 100 per cent successful. Most authorities had a steam disinfector, as contact with smallpox cases was not uncommon, necessitating the disinfection of clothing, bedding, etc."

Mr Hacker recalls using the methylene blue test to check the microbiological quality of milk products, particularly ice cream: "These were the days of corner shops making their own ice cream." The 1950s, he remembers, brought the Food Hygiene Regulations and the need to bring a myriad of food premises up to standard. "Much later," he adds, "came food hygiene training courses, in which our own profession played a signicant role."

George Hart was called up for national service in 1946. Aged 19, he took the field hygiene course at the RAMC at Camberley in Surrey and served as a corporal in the Indian Field Hygiene Section HQ in Mandalay, Burma.

He writes: "When I was demobilised in 1948, there was a severe shortage of inspectors. To fill the gap a government-sponsored training scheme was launched. Following a gruelling interview at the Ministry of Health, I won a place on a course at the Royal Technical College, Salford. I had my fees paid and received a monthly maintenance payment of £20. For two years,

National serviceman George Hart (second from left, front row) with the Indian Field Hygiene Section

I spent four days a week undergoing practical training, attached to various local authorities, and one day at college."

Mr Hart was aiming to obtain the meat inspectors' certificate, the City and Guilds Boiler House practical exam and the National Certificate in Mechanical Engineering and to pass the Institute of Public Cleansing's examination. "Times were tough in the late-1940s and early-1950s," he writes, "but I was content with a salary of £390. My professional career was mainly sorting out problems that the other agencies could not deal with."

Another national serviceman, Graham H Smith, recalls how he had specified his ideal occupation to a careers adviser while still at school: "Paid employment as a student for a technical profession, requiring the wearing of a suit, without office containment and with the future provision of a car." He says: "The lady advisor said 'sanitary inspector' was the only profession which met my specification. I said, 'that will do me'. I received £2.50 per week and was the first person in the country to go on a weekly day-release college course."

Rodney Lamb started at Middleton Corporation's sanitary department in 1948, aged 16, attended Manchester Technical College for three years, did national service with the RAF for two years and then returned to Middleton. He qualified as a sanitary inspector in 1954. "My senior inspector was Mr Fred Potter, a wonderful person. We dealt with Ancoats, Miles Platting, Newton Heath and Moston. Many of the houses were awaiting demolition. I was told to expect anything… In one case, it was claimed that every time the WC was flushed, the light went out. This was ignored as nonsense but it was found to be true."

Wilson Hargreaves had begun as a trainee sanitary inspector for Lancaster's health department, aged 16. One of his tasks was fumigating with formaldehyde gas isolation wards for infectious diseases such as diphtheria, pulmonary tuberculosis, puerperal pyrexia and scarlet fever. This was achieved by adding water to tins of dry ingredients, using gummed paper rolls to seal off rooms. This was not easy in the case of double swing doors: "With tears running down my face, I in some way managed a rough seal."

On 5 November, 1942, aged 18, he was called up. "After six weeks' infantry training, I was assigned as a Bren gun carrier driver. 'What do you do in civvie street?' 'I'm training as a sanitary inspector.' 'Just the man we want. Report to the RAMC tradesman's hut.' Then the Army School of Hygiene at Mytchett for a two-month course. Now corporal, an instructor on water supplies for sanitation in the field. Each fortnight, 500 service men and women arrived at the school. I was speaking to the gathering on lice – head, body and pubic – when one Canadian soldier spoke out. 'Corporal, in Canada, we call pubic lice mobile dandruff.' Next, 12 volunteers were required for the 74th Field Hygiene Section in the newly formed 6th Airborne Division: no volunteers – stand up all single men. I was in!"

Mr Hargreaves landed by glider in France and worked in a field dressing station as D-Day advanced. He crossed the Rhine and was later posted to Haifa, Palestine. His numerous vivid recollections include spraying DDT from a flame-thrower and powdering refugees with DDT. Demobbed, he returned to Lancaster's health department under Fred Shaw to resume his long career.

FD Marriott was a sanitary assistant in the RAMC, serving as an instructor in the Army School of Hygiene, where he taught thousands of servicemen the skills of disease control and water purification – a recruiting ground for technical assistants and sanitary inspectors. Immediately after the war, he worked in a delousing station in Cologne, with a throughput of thousands, requiring 14-hour days. "I believe that typhus, then raging in Warsaw and nearby areas, was prevented from spreading to the west by such programmes, an unsung part of the aftermath of the war. Huge hospitals, previously used as isolation units, were disinfected by British army personnel."

He writes: "Later, I became civilian-qualified and began my career in earnest. The inspection of meat was a main part of our daily task and the subsequent gross reduction in mortality rates was very rewarding." He remembers when TB was an unmentionable condition bringing social stigma, rickets was 'the English disease', tons of particulate matter fell from the sky and bronchitis was normal, recalling that "the sanitary inspector was an honoured figure in most northern towns".

Demobbed in 1945, Eric Silvester was one of a select few offered a paid place on a full-time sanitary inspectors' course at London University. He writes: "We entered the profession at the sharp end… We did anything and everything, at times dirty, smelly, dangerous and frustrating but our job of 'putting wrong things right' was surely one of the best and all for £360 a year plus £30 London weighting. We were there! I have many memories but I vividly remember my uncle Fred (who had been gassed while serving as a soldier in World War One) dying soon after the Great Smog in great distress, with the complexion of lead."

After taking a diploma at Salford Technical College, Brian Mayers served in the Royal Navy until 1948. He served on the aircraft carrier *HMS Implacable,* which formed part of the escort to George VI, the Queen Mother and princesses Elizabeth and Margaret on their visit to South Africa aboard *HMS Vanguard.*

Following his naval experiences, he passed a Ministry of Health interview to undertake a training course for ex-servicemen. He worked in Luton, Chesterfield and Macclesfield and retired in 1986 as deputy borough EHO at Hyndburn MBC in Lancashire. He reflects: "I started as a sanitary inspector, which, in the public eye, was not far removed from the old job of inspector of nuisances. Thankfully, the post-war intake into the profession could see the prospects for a respected group of officers to play a full part in local authority affairs. Progress was made in our roles as public health inspectors to our present day standing as members of a respected Chartered Institute."

His professional recollections are vivid, including the battle for smoke control in Oswaldtwistle (later absorbed into Hyndburn) as its chief public health inspector and its slum clearance programmes, originally using powers under 1957 legislation that continued into the 1960s. Slum clearance was surprisingly controversial. In a case that must have been duplicated all over the country, an Oswaldtwistle Tenants, Owner Occupiers and Property Association was set up. It conducted a campaign to protect from demolition a group of houses in Union Road, which had been declared 'unfit' by the council. The group portrayed council officials as high-handed bureaucrats indifferent to their wishes. The case went to the housing and local government minister for appeal and four houses were reprieved.

Public health inspectors had to be even-handed in such matters and the best were adept at using the media. In one story, Mr Mayers told the local paper: "I cannot accept that two-up, two-down cottages, many with rising damp, waste water closets and without hot water and bathrooms, are suitable housing conditions." In another, he is reported as urging councillors to "forget bureaucracy" and to keep human feelings uppermost in their minds when re-housing people as part of

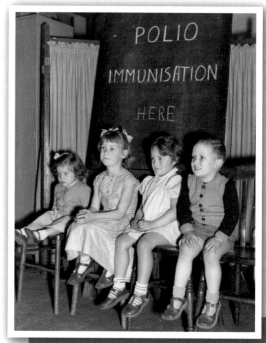

Mass immunistation helped to eradicate polio as a childhood illness

redevelopment schemes. Attacked by residents and councillors alike, it seems that he was stuck in the middle – a position familiar to many inspectors.

There was plenty to keep him busy – for example, improving private water supplies on moorlands, where animals were grazed, and, in crowded urban areas, visiting the homes of those with TB, scarlet fever and, in one case, polio to assess their housing conditions and to help prevent the illness from spreading. "The polio case caused a stir. The precautions taken – mainly the issuing of the polio vaccine on sugar lumps – were carefully monitored by our medical officer of health, Dr Reginald Webster. He was Brain of Britain on radio and TV, a wonderful, kind man who supported me in various issues over the years.

Mr Mayers also recalls that "Oswaldtwistle introduced me to a new problem – the supply direct to the public of raw milk." He found that people in north-east Lancashire were becoming infected with brucellosis from this source. He increased the sampling of herds linked to contaminated milk and tried to persuade farmers – not always successfully, for there was no legal requirement – to send affected animals to slaughter. His efforts and the denial of farmers that raw milk was unsafe received extensive coverage in the local and occasionally national press. National Farmers Union officials vigorously refuted that there was any danger from unpasteurised milk. Mr Mayers knew better. Vets, too, he recalls, "took some time to accept that animal health and human health were closely aligned".

Adeline K Lewis, who was to become a secretary, chair and London Centre president and to sit on the then IEHO's General Council, was one of only a few women to enter what was then a male-dominated domain. She recalls: "In 1946, when I came out of the services, I had to struggle to be accepted on an ex-service sanitary inspectors' course. The interviewing board tried very hard to convince me that I should train as a nurse and become a health visitor. I was the only woman in a class of 30. When I qualified and was appointed to Manchester's public health department, I was one of only two 'lady inspectors' and was permitted to inspect the homes of outworkers employed by the numerous textile factories. I was not allowed to do other general duties… when I retired in 1982, it was gratifying to see how many more women were coming into the profession."

Andrew Banfield, who later served as national president of the Chartered Institute of Environmental Health, was appointed as a student public health inspector at the Royal Borough of Kensington in 1959. He had taken his certificate over four years at the Brixton School of Building and then at South East London Technical College, and was a contemporary of Ned Kingcott, who later served as chief EHO at the Department of Health, and John Tiffney, who was also to become national president of his professional body.

He recalls: "We rarely saw our medical officer of health. Our direct manager, the chief public health inspector, was a formidable figure who led the inspectorate with military discipline. This was not surprising as most of the PHIs had been in the armed forces, including most of my predecessors as students. Indeed, I was the youngest student ever taken on and regarded as the 'boy' and an experiment. Many of the PHIs were characters and able by their own personalities to achieve public health improvements without statutory action.

"Formal dress and behaviour were normal. Indeed, I remember a few inspectors still wore homburgs or bowler hats. Most inspectors worked in geographical districts grouped in small teams led by senior inspectors. There was a small number of senior inspectors who operated borough-wide. Evening and weekend working was common."

Maurice Duffield, who worked in Salford, concurs on antisocial hours. He writes: "Tuberculosis in cattle was not uncommon in the 1950s and often found when carrying out meat inspection in slaughterhouses… Meat inspection often had to be carried out at unsociable hours as, very often, a slaughterman would knock on my door at 10pm to indicate that slaughtering had finished. I would then have to go and inspect 80 to 100 pigs to enable them to be loaded up and delivered the next day. Meat inspectors, trained to assist public health inspectors, were not introduced until the 1970s."

Geoffrey Lindsey remembers working in Belfast in the 1950s: "Sanitary officers, as we were called then, were referred to in Northern Ireland as 'the sanitary'. They were the men from the town hall who would come to your house and clear a choked gully in the back yard, fumigate a bedroom after infectious disease, or get rid of rats and mice if there was an infestation. The salary was £380 per year.

"In 1951, in order to improve our social position, the Belfast public health department decreed that every sanitary officer must wear a bowler hat on duty. This prevailed for about a year and it caused intense resentment among staff, with the result that, gradually, it was no longer obeyed and we reverted to other hats or went hatless."

Housing

The urban landscape of the early 1950s would appear alien to a person magically transported from the present. Much by-law housing from the 19th century survived, particularly in the north, in rows of monotonous terraces. Britain's towns, cities and ports had been pummelled by bombing – it is estimated that the country came out of the war with 200,000 houses destroyed and more than three million damaged. Waiting lists for council housing often ran into the thousands and the acuteness of the housing shortage was a topic that preoccupied the press and politicians.

Ron Charnick gives us a vivid description of Southwark in south London, where 100,000 people occupied 1,100 acres: "Littered with bomb sites, overcrowded, badly damaged, poorly repaired and much unfit housing. Four licensed common lodging houses for 300 men and women each night. Overrun with rats both within and outside public sewers, needing 12 rodent operatives to control. No DDT so infestations of bed bugs, fleas, lice and cockroaches prevalent requiring treatments in a large bathing station for personal hygiene and article disinfection. Air pollution was heavy. However, work was available in markets and shops and most railway arches had businesses. Large-scale industrial and commercial work was also available. Much imported food from ships at Bankside."

Things weren't much better north of the river in Hackney. Norman Jackson writes: "Reports about elderly people came in from concerned neighbours that some were living in insanitary conditions, typically occupying a basement flat, were poorly nourished, cold and surrounded by a build-up of old clothing, newspapers and other memories of past times. The build-up was usually of some four feet or so... The smell and air of Dickensian neglect was strong. The only water supply was a shallow sink and a cold, miserable toilet could be reached from the outside. Something needed to be done."

Ewan Holt recalls of Salford that its inner-city housing could only be classed as slums. "The district inspector," he recalls, "would spend at least three-quarters of his time walking around his patch dealing with a continuous flow of complaints from tenants. It was very much an uphill, never-ending task, usually involving statutory action and court attendances. Many landlords abandoned their property, requiring default action by the local authority.

Before slum clearance schemes many houses had outdoor WCs, often shared

"There were still back-to-back houses, row upon row of terraced houses and, in the oldest parts, ill-drained common yards serving eight or nine houses, all using one dilapidated WC, houses with outside taps and slopstones for sinks – conditions unimaginable today... To make matters worse for the poor souls who had to live in such conditions, they had to breathe smoke-polluted air as well. With thousands of domestic chimneys and factories pouring out smoke into the atmosphere, it was no wonder there was a great deal of respiratory illness; chronic bronchitis being commonplace."

Ron Coebe corroborates this vivid picture of a smoky, damp and overcrowded North-West. He writes: "The majority of houses comprised two ground-floor living rooms, one of which contained a shallow, earthenware sink with a cold water tap, and two first-floor rooms. Gas lighting was provided to the ground floor rooms only and cooking was generally by a small cast-iron combination grate, coal-fired of course.

"Rising and penetrating dampness were widespread and sanitary accommodation was a water closet in a small rear yard… As a profession, we struggled to keep such premises at least watertight and in reasonable repair until they could be demolished and their occupants re-housed. This improvement of the national housing stock is one of the finest achievements of the CIEH and I am proud to have a played a small part in it."

Widespread slum clearance was ushered in by the Conservatives' 1954 Housing, Repairs and Rents Act. This led to the demolition of tens of thousands of back-to-back terraced houses with shared external WCs. As well as slum-clearance and energetic council-house building, Conservative governments of the 1950s are remembered for relaxing rent controls, theorising that this would stimulate the supply of private rented housing.

It was a double-edged sword, giving private landlords a strong incentive to get rid of sitting tenants. The era is strongly associated with the abuses of slum landlord Peter Rachman, who is taken as a representative of all of them and leant his name to a noun – 'Rachmanism'. Rachman's area of north-west London attracted large-scale immigration throughout the 1950s – many of his tenants were Afro-Caribbeans who some white landlords refused to house. In September 1958, complex social issues led to London and Britain's first race riots in Notting Hill.

Kenneth Mahers, a district inspector in Paddington, remembers Rachman's reign of fear: "He would exploit and intimidate the tenants, try the same tactics on officials, ignore notices and switch companies to avoid compliance. I would at times be on the district until after 9pm with residents queuing to register their complaints… on one occasion, a car came alongside and two of Rachman's henchmen grabbed me and wanted to know which properties I had visited and why. They said I should just keep my mouth, ears and eyes closed. Was I a police informer?"

Andrew Banfield describes similar experiences in North Kensington: "The housing shortage contributed to the rise of Rachmanism. Some private landlords ruthlessly exploited the situation and soon we were overwhelmed, trying to help these tenants with inadequate resources. I met many of these landlords and they were not pleasant characters. Their basic strategy was to force out tenants with some form of security of tenure and replace them with new tenants who could be forced to pay much higher rents."

If there was political consensus about the need to build new housing, this did not apply to how to deal with the existing housing stock and private landlords. The opposition Labour party, led by Hugh Gaitskill, pledged to repeal the Rent Act of 1957 and to reintroduce rent control. It was still official Labour policy that all private rented housing should be brought into municipal ownership. This policy was derided by the Conservatives, along with Labour's proposed land, or 'betterment', tax as akin to Bolshevism.

Smoke control

Poor air quality was a major contributor to morbidity in the 1950s. There were three main causes: Britain's still-productive manufacturing industries, coal-fired power stations and a heavy domestic use of coal. Alan Shankster writes: "As a child going to school in the 1940s and early 1950s in the outer suburbs of Leeds, I well remember the thick smogs which caused my asthma. I realised that the source was coal smoke whilst servicing the pollution measurement instruments at Leeds City health department as a student in the 1960s."

Dense 'pea souper' fogs were finally eliminated by the Clean Air Act of 1956

An infamous cold snap in London in December 1952 produced a toxic 'pea souper' fog that lingered for days and caused a huge number of premature deaths. At first, there was little response. Harold MacMillan fobbed off the House of Commons with talk of the complexity and expense of cleaning up air quality. A committee, chaired by engineer Sir Hugh Beaver, found a shocking winter mortality rate in Britain from lung ailments and recommended solutions. Finally, it was a private member's bill from Kidderminster MP Gerald Nabarro that pricked a reluctant government into action. Four years after the great London smog came the milestone Clean Air Act of 1956.

Jack Fish, who was sanitary inspector for the county borough of West Ham, remembers the London winter of 1952. "Visibility, even in the daytime, was so bad that I remember bus inspectors carrying flares and walking in front of trolley buses in Stratford Broadway to guide them into position. The health implications of those few days were far-reaching. It caused many hundreds and possibly thousands of deaths through bronchial and cardiac conditions in London. Politicians were shocked into the action that our profession had been calling-for for years."

David J Wells describes how bad the air was in Fulham in the early-1950s: "I can remember being on the roof of a high building and realising that such was the poor air quality, I could see no more than yards, everything just vanished in the smog. When I drove home that night, part of my journey was guided by a policeman carrying a flare. The price of such living was that life expectation was much less than we see today. The average working man, if he was lucky, worked until he was 65 and 'did his duty' and died when he was 68. His wife lived a little longer."

In the Midlands and North, heavy industry increased even further the burden of soot, particulate matter and sulphur dioxide. Recalling Salford in the 1950s, Maurice Duffield writes: "There were many industrial chimneys together with thousands of domestic flues. I can remember being in the centre of Manchester one lunchtime when suddenly the whole area was blacked with thick smog. I thought at the time it was the end of the world! All traffic stopped and flamed torches were ignited to indicate traffic junctions and islands. I had great difficulty in finding my way back to my digs."

And in Liverpool? "My early memories, especially during winter months, was the soot and sulphuric acid-laden air blackening buildings," writes AS Crowe. "I saw the results during my work in the city abattoir... black soot deposits were found in the lungs of slaughtered cows."

After the Clean Air Act was passed, councils rushed to declare smoke control areas, but it was often not easy to enforce them. C Wilks helped to introduce one of England's largest smoke control areas – more than a thousand acres of central Leeds. He remembers: "Explaining the benefits of a smoke control area was like selling sand to the Arabs. Putting it mildly, the occupants of houses were not impressed, especially when we used the chilling phrase, 'You will not be allowed to burn coal.' We followed that up with the magic words: 'There will be a grant to replace your fireplace with an appliance to burn smokeless fuels'."

Many now retired inspectors feel justly proud of the practical role they played in bringing about smoke control. Adrian Lord writes: "As a junior public health inspector in Rochdale, I spent time helping Bill Garside, the senior PHI, to implement the programme in the town. Through his sheer doggedness and determination, the programme was successfully completed, bringing about a transformation of the environmental conditions of the borough.

"Initially, there was opposition to the programme, particularly reservations about more limited reductions in sulphur dioxide and fears about potential shortages of smokeless fuels. But they were overcome. I would contend that, on a national basis, the smoke control programme eventually resulted in the single largest improvement in environmental conditions this country has seen. The killer smogs were consigned to history and this was especially thanks to the diligent work of PHIs throughout the country."

Coventry's pioneer

Arthur Harrison writes: "The 1950 and 1960s brought in ground-breaking health legislation that led to major improvements in housing, cleaner air, safer food and water services. In 1951, Coventry City Council appointed Ronald Williams as chief sanitary inspector. Mr Williams was to become a pioneer in improving both the status of our profession and the health of the community.

"At that time, the medical officer of health, Dr Clayton, was in charge of a large range of services, including the sanitary inspectorate. However, Mr Williams persuaded the council to make him head of the city's public health department. This was a period of great change for the city. Coventry had been heavily bombed by the German Luftwaffe on 14 November, 1940. The city had lost many homes and its historic St Michael's Cathedral had been gutted.

Coventry City's public health department was headed by Ronald Williams, shown fourth from left, front row

"King George VI had made a personal visit two days later to see the damage and to show the Royal Family's support for the people of Coventry. It was therefore appropriate that Queen Elizabeth should lay the foundation stone of the new cathedral on 23 March, 1956. She was again present when the cathedral was finally consecrated on 25 May, 1962, making 2012 its Golden Jubilee.

"The city's public health inspectors played an important but little publicised part in the building of the new cathedral. It was their job to supervise and monitor the opening and relocation of the graves before the building could start. The new cathedral symbolised Coventry's resurgence, but the city's post-war success brought challenges, too.

"In the 1950s and 1960s, Coventry was still a large industrial centre. More workers were needed than were available locally and as a result, there was a huge influx of people. Coventry became known as the city paved with gold. To accommodate the workers, homes were often occupied by day with one set and at night by another. The local public health inspectors found themselves responsible for inspecting homes in multiple occupation on a grand scale. Large council housing estates were built to provide for families, including those removed from slum clearance areas.

"To make it easier for his staff to travel around the city, Ronald Williams replaced their bicycles with small, 125cc motorcycles. Later, he brought in mileage allowances, which enabled inspectors to use their own cars. In the 1950s, Mr Williams made the centre of Coventry the first smokeless zone in the country. He went on to introduce smoke-control areas, thus substantially reducing a product known as smog – a dangerous mixture of smoke and fog.

"Machinery such as road breakers used in the redevelopment of the city centre generated excessive noise. Mr Williams served noise-abatement notices on the operators and, initially, this almost caused work to stop. However, his logic – that contractors would apply themselves to reducing noise levels – proved to be correct.

"When food hygiene legislation came into force, a decision was made to challenge the practices of a national fishmonger, MacFisheries. The aim was to establish the effectiveness of the regulations. The resulting court case was inconclusive. As a result, food sampling and analysis were made a priority in the city.

"This work highlighted the presence of lead in vegetables that had been grown near busy highways and therefore exposed to the fumes from petrol engines. The findings prompted Mr Williams to test the air for lead. Results confirmed the widespread presence of lead, which we now know was probably responsible for health problems, especially in young children.

"Testing of river water pinpointed where industrial pollutants were being discharged. This resulted in enforcement action and a gradual improvement in water quality. By this time, there were fewer and fewer working boats on the canals, and the water authorities wanted to close them. However, the inspections required by the Canal Boat Regulations continued and the efforts of an active lobby group led to the development of the canal boat leisure industry we know today.

"Ronald Williams died at our annual conference, on 9 October, 1960. His lasting contribution to the work of our profession and the wellbeing of our society was later honoured by the presentation of an annual award in his name."

Filth and vermin

As the result of a misguided sense of propriety, women were often shielded from the dirtiest duties. But, in the 1950s, sanitary inspectors were expected to do work that other people would shy away from. On a human level, their job could involve dealing with violently inclined landlords and recalcitrant business operators. Tact and good people skills were required. And a strong stomach.

Both urban and rural settings offered ample opportunities for revulsion – sorting out privies and middens, peering into drains, dealing with rats, inspecting the local abattoirs, meat renderers or maggot farms and supervising exhumations in graveyards. Sanitary inspection was a unique role, requiring its practitioners to know something of the law, animal pathology, microbiology and the chemistry of toxins and pollutants and to be able to lift a manhole cover.

David Beardmore remembers his work for Marple Urban District Council, near Manchester, in 1956. He notes: "Our role was varied. In addition to meat hygiene duties we had to look after refuse collection and disposal services, and also to manage the letting of council property. One of the services was to provide a vehicle on which was fitted a large metal tank. This was to deal with sanitary disposal operations every week. There were throughout the borough waste disposal facilities, such as pail closets, ash pits, cesspools and septic tanks, all requiring regular attention."

As a student public health inspector in Ossett, West Yorkshire, in 1959, Brian Fox cycled 10 miles for his first day at work where he faced some fairly unpalatable tasks: "Upon arrival, the boss said to me, 'At some time I will have to teach you pest control, so go down to the basement, mix the poison baits and go to treat the rat infestation at the sewage works.' I duly mixed the bait, put the tin in my saddlebag and carried out the treatment. Later, I visited our refuse tip and gaped wide-eyed at a discarded opened food tin. It was absolutely full of crickets. The tip was sprayed with insecticide and sacks soaked with it were placed on the surface to finish the treatment.

"At one time, we had to clear a blocked drain. The manhole cover was lifted. It was absolutely full to the brim with sewage and we had to endure a terrible stench. After rodding the drain, the manhole contents suddenly started to move and disappeared. The occupants of the house were very relieved.

"Near to the house was a small, two-slab mortuary, which our office was responsible for cleaning. I was given the keys during the day and told to go round on my own. When I questioned this, the chief said, 'Don't worry as there is only one body in there and it will

Pest baiting was a common task for the student sanitary or public health inspector

be covered by a sheet.' Needless to say, I opted out of that one and spent the time looking in local shop windows before returning to the office."

The floods

As they do today, inspectors had to deal with the environmental and public health consequences of one-off events, whether these were large-scale outbreaks of disease or disasters. In February 1953, in the early days of Elizabeth's reign, flooding devastated the east coast of England. Caused by a storm surge, it was the UK's largest ever natural disaster, causing more than 300 deaths.

George Mills worked in Harwich, Essex, a small authority at the epicentre of the event. He recalls: "On the night of 31 January, there was an exceptionally high tide and strong winds and two tidal waves resulted in large areas of the east coast being flooded. One of the towns affected was Harwich.

Flooding on the east coast of England in 1953 was the UK's worst natural disaster

"The main pumping station was in the middle of a flooded area and all pumps were inoperable. Harwich was a small authority with limited staff but all were required for this emergency. The sanitary inspector took a key role from the start and many outside and voluntary agencies were involved.

"Evacuation of the flooded properties was the immediate priority. This became critical because of the weather conditions. It was undertaken in many cases by boat as the only means of transport. Many people were accommodated with friends and family, but a large number had to be accommodated in public halls. As it became clear that many would not be able to return to their homes for a considerable time, temporary accommodation in the form of mobile homes was provided."

Because of the scale of tasks required, inspectors were drafted in from surrounding areas. They were kept busy for many months. What followed will be familiar to today's environmental health practitioners dealing with emergencies and disasters – inspecting houses to identify emergency repairs, such as restoring services; visiting food premises to make sure that flood-damaged stock was disposed of; removing vast quantities of waste and rubbish; checking water supplies and supplying disinfectants.

Jack Fish was working in West Ham in East London. He remembers: "At that time, the Royal Docks were still in use by sea-going cargo ships... It was the low-lying areas of Silver Town and Canning Town that bore the brunt of the flooding. As soon as the sewage-contaminated water receded, all of us were sent into the areas to assess the damage to personal belongings for limited government compensation and to issue vouchers for tenants to claim a hundredweight of coal to assist in drying out their houses."

The services

As we have seen, there is a strong tradition of environmental health practitioners working in the armed services and this has continued throughout the Queen's reign. The role of environmental health is a vital factor in the protection of fighting units in the field. Working with the three services, the CIEH facilitated the development of an accredited degree programme and supported the training and development of their environmental health function as it grew in strength and importance in the post-war period.

In 2007, retired EHO Barrie Sheard, himself a former national serviceman, placed an advertisement in *EHN*, calling for reminiscences from other CIEH members of their national service days in the Army, Royal Navy and RAF.

His request yielded a healthy response – more than 69 replies and many photographs spanning the period from the 1940s to the 1960s. The memories were collected into albums and burned onto CDs. These were presented to the CIEH at a special ceremony at Chadwick Court, attended by 50 former sanitary and public health inspectors and serving army EHPs and technicians with their commanding officers.

In 2012, the year of the Queen's Diamond Jubilee, there were approximately 40 EHPs serving in the Army, Royal Navy and RAF and around 120 technicians, the majority in the Army. When not deployed, EHPs in the services deal with similar issues to their civilian colleagues, such as food safety and occupational health and safety. Operations expose them to additional challenges concerning sanitation and tropical disease, often in extreme climates.

A long-standing tradition is a tri-services conference, held every two years, for EHPs and technicians from all three services, at which they share experiences and hear presentations from experts. Each of the services has a lead EHO and one of them is also appointed as the defence trade specialist EHO.

In 2012, the head of army environmental health and DTSO was Lieutenant Colonel Andrew Charnick. He began his army career as a staff clerk in the Royal Army Ordnance Corps, before transferring to the Royal Army Medical Corps and qualifying as an EHO in 1992. He became a CIEH member in 2009. His career took him to the Americas, all over Europe, Asia, the Middle East and Africa and embraced all levels of seniority, through to commanding the health unit in Cyprus and posts in the Ministry of Defence.

Major Gareth Moore graduated in environmental health from King's College London. He began his army career at the RAMC and worked as a military environmental health technician in Central America, Kenya, the Falkland Islands, Bosnia and during the first Gulf War. His deployments included Afghanistan, Iraq, Kosovo and Sierra Leone. In 2012, he was employed as commanding officer for the military environmental health training school.

He writes: "My main effort is to ensure that troops are as well prepared as possible to overcome the health threats on operational deployment. There is a real sense of achievement and satisfaction working as a military EHP – be that controlling a disease outbreak in austere conditions with minimal resources, or attending the graduation of the next generation of military EHPs, knowing that the lessons learned from current operations are not going to be forgotten."

Unlike the Royal Navy and the RAF, the Army has a reserve environmental health component. The senior EHP in that group in 2012 was Geoff Ward, EHP, Bath and North East Somerset councillor and chairman of CIEH Ltd.

He signed up for the regulars in 1974 from school and trained as a hygiene assistant with the Royal Army Medical Corps at Keogh Barracks, Ash Vale, Surrey. He then went on to join the Territorial Army Field Hygiene Platoon based at Mytchett Place, in the barracks where Rudolph Hess was held.

This gave him a taste for environmental health in civvy street and he took his diploma at Salford College of Technology, working as a student EHO at Manchester in the environmental health department headed by Eric Foskett. He says: "The first year, I worked as a drainage examiner and pest control officer. Talk about starting at the bottom of the profession!"

After qualifying in 1981, Mr Ward continued his TA service alongside his environmental health career. The commitment involved one two-week camp and six weekends per year with foreign attachments in Germany, Belgium and Cyprus. He joined Trust House Forte in 1984 as regional safety manager in the South-West. In 1984, he was commissioned as a Lieutenant EHO into 219 field hospital in Keynsham, Bristol.

In 1988, he set up an environmental health consultancy supporting the hospitality industry, HMS Ltd. After the successful sale of the business in 2007, Mr Ward, now a TA major, moved to the 2nd Medical Brigade based at York and took on a medical intelligence role with an attachment to the Ministry of Defence in London, providing tutoring and advice support to NATO. In 2012, he was promoted to Lieutenant Colonel, becoming the most senior EHP in the Territorial Army.

He says: "It's a great achievement for me personally and it's good for the profession, because it shows how valuable and transferable our EHP skills are. My role is with the new operational headquarters support group co-ordinating an EH team providing medical force protection. Under government plans, reserve EHPs will have a greater role to forces deployed overseas and in the UK. This is an interesting time for the reserves as they develop their new capabilities."

Another serving EHP and lead for the Royal Navy in 2012 was Lieutenant Warren Haynes, who left his role as a local authority environmental health manager to join the Navy. He undertook officer training at Britannia Royal Naval College in Dartmouth and took sea-fighting and survival courses. He served on a destroyer, *HMS York*, and a fishery protection vessel, before joining the occupational health teams at navy bases in Portsmouth and Plymouth. He says: "I dealt with pest control, port health, drinking water, food safety, public health, communicable disease and living conditions in ships and onshore establishments."

In 2011, he volunteered for a six-month deployment to Afghanistan, working in Kabul, Kandahar, Lashkar Gar and other forward bases, where he assessed health threats with colleagues and carried out security assessments of food and water supplies. Describing his career as a uniformed EHP as "diverse and tremendously rewarding", he returned to the UK to join the medical division of the Royal Navy's command HQ in Portsmouth.

Lt. Warren Haynes, EHP, was deployed by the Royal Navy in Kabul, Afghanistan in 2011

Squadron Leader Gary Moyes began his career in environmental health in the RAF in 1993 and qualified as a registered EHP in 2003. He was deployed to many locations, including Afghanistan, Iraq, the Middle East and the Falkland Islands and carried out a number of roles, including that of station environmental health technician. In 2012, he became responsible for delivering an environmental health service to the whole of the RAF in the UK and overseas.

He explains: "It is the variety of roles in the services that makes being an EHP so interesting and rewarding. One is protecting the health of a whole population of personnel by applying simple environmental health principles. Interventions can range from basic sanitary advice in austere locations to undertaking detailed occupational hygiene assessments as part of a specialist monitoring team."

Chronology 1950s

1952

February Death of King George VI. HRH Elizabeth II becomes Queen.

■ Winston Churchill heads a Conservative Government elected the previous year. Rab Butler is chancellor. Harold Macmillan, housing minister, is entrusted with a pledge to build 300,000 houses a year.

■ British troops fly into Kenya. Britain tests its first atom bomb.

■ Following war damage, the census shows one million more households than dwellings and more than two million dwellings shared.

■ Ministry of Housing and Local Government set up (formerly called local government and planning). Housing Act allows councils to sell houses.

1953

February Hurricane winds flood the east coast.

2 June Televised coronation of Queen Elizabeth II in Westminster Abbey watched by 20 million people. TVs are owned by 2.5 million people and cost, on average, £85.

■ Housing white paper proposes cancelling rent controls and reducing housing subsidies in the public sector. 318,000 houses are built. Production peaks in 1954 at 357,000 (a quarter of which are in the private sector).

1954

■ Housing Repairs and Rents Act. New private lets removed from rent control. Councils can take over slums for site value. Abolition of building licences. Labour's opposition policy is that all private sector rented housing should be municipalised – five to six million homes.

■ Butter and meat rationing end. Sweet rationing a year later. Mars bars cost 4d.

■ 40,000 immigrants arrive. There is no race relations legislation.

1955

April Winston Churchill stands down as Prime Minister, due to ill health, aged 80. Anthony Eden (pictured), his chosen successor, takes over. In May, Eden wins an election for the Conservatives.

■ Hugh Gaitskell follows Clement Attlee as leader of the Labour party.

■ Commercial television begins.

■ Average week earnings are now £11, up from £7 in 1950. By 1964, they are £18.

■ Food and Drugs Act, to prevent sale of food unfit for human consumption.

1956

■ Uprising in Hungary. Suez crisis. Eden resigns. Rab Butler, leader of the House, takes temporary charge.

■ Housing minister Duncan Sandys reduces then abolishes the subsidy for council housing. Subsidies are retained for slum clearance and new towns.

■ Sandys introduces an 'extra height subsidy' for blocks above five storeys (abolished in 1967). By 1966, high-rises are a quarter of the construction programme.

■ Clean Air Act passed.

1957

January Macmillan becomes PM, aged 62, when Eden resigns. He says: "Most of our people have never had it so good."

March Founding of the European Common Market, by France, West Germany, Italy, Belgium, Holland and Luxembourg in the Treaty of Rome.

October Windscale fire, the worst nuclear accident in Britain.

■ Campaign for Nuclear Disarmament begins.

■ Rent Act. De-controls rents. Attacked by Labour.

■ Housing Act. Powers on slum clearance and housing improvement areas and grants.

■ Association of Public Sanitary Inspectors is renamed the Association of Public Health Inspectors.

1958

April First CND march from London to Aldermaston.

September Race riots in London's Notting Hill. Fifty-nine people are arrested.

1959

September Macmillan calls an election. Conservatives win their third in a row. Macmillan known as 'Supermac' promises no nationalisation. Rab Butler is chancellor.

■ Driest summer for 200 years.

■ National Insurance Act. State pensions graduated according to salary level.

■ Alton Estate. London County Council scheme, in south-west London. Mixed housing, integrated with its landscape – a template for 1960s council housing.

■ First section of the M1, Britain's first motorway is opened.

LONDON-B'HAM

MOTORWAY AT LAST!

The 1960s

White
heat

The 1960s saw the UK in social and technological transition. Sanitary inspectors were public health inspectors now, but they were often still dealing with poor air quality and with primitive living conditions that harked back to the 1930s. The decade's political watershed came in 1964. A new Prime Minister, Harold Wilson, who was from Huddersfield and had attended a grammar school, brought to the job an engaging man-in-the street manner and a northern accent (in contrast to the mandarin vowels of Harold Macmillan and Sir Alec Douglas-Home). Mr Wilson promised to usher in a new meritocracy and the 'white heat of technology'.

The country had been revolted by Rachamanism. Labour introduced security of tenure and rent control in its first two years. The dash to build council housing continued, but there was still a huge under-supply, and councils were often remote and autocratic landlords. In 1966, an influential television play, *Cathy Come Home*, led to lobbying for better treatment of homeless people and to the creation of the campaigning charity Shelter. In the 1960s, race relations matured, rights were accorded to gypsies and travellers and noise abatement legislation arrived.

After the Buchanan Report of 1963, town planning was dominated by provision for the car. The decade saw the arrival of the shopping mall, the dramatic rise of the supermarket and a huge expansion of the motorway network.

Two environmental disasters were brought into the nation's living rooms through the powerful medium of television. The appalling collapse of the Aberfan colliery tip in Wales in 1966 smothered 116 children and 28 adults (see below). The following year, the *Torrey Canyon* oil tanker disaster, spilling thousands of tons of crude oil into the sea off the coast of Cornwall, brought to television screens for the first time images of oiled seabirds. In the same year, foot and mouth disease rampaged through the Midlands and North Wales, leading to the slaughter of half a million animals. Despite the two-volume Northumberland report, few lessons appear to have been learned from this outbreak. When foot and mouth returned later in the Queen's reign in 2001, its effects were even more devastating. In the human health domain, the 1960s saw the UK's last outbreaks of smallpox and typhoid (see below).

It was also a decade of ambitious and unselfconscious local authority building projects, with large blocks of flats built, often using prefabrication – an iconic version being Sheffield's Park Hill Estate (the flats were grade II-listed by English Heritage in 1998 and survive to the present day). In Newcastle, the council's charismatic leader, T Dan Smith was putting huge efforts into planning, slum clearance and high-rise building. He seemed to be a man for the age – a miner's son who had risen by his own efforts to a position of civic and political leadership. In 1962, his public relations firm, which was promoting re-development across the north, formed a relationship with Wandsworth-based architect, John Poulson.

The collapse of Ronan Point in 1968 symbolised the end of an era

Both men were subsequently convicted and jailed for giving and receiving bribes.

The collapse of a 22-storey, system-built tower block, Ronan Point, in Canning Town in May 1968 following a small gas explosion was seen at the time as a visual metaphor for corruption, providing a symbolic end to the high-rise era. In fact, it did not fizzle out until the following decade, but the mood was shifting from building to restoration. In 1969, of great relevance to public health inspectors, came general improvement areas, mandatory home improvement grants and powers on houses in multiple occupation.

The Association of Public Health Inspectors remained at Grosvenor Place, with Reginald Johnson as general secretary. Membership grew by a fifth over the decade, from 5,000 in 1960 to 6,000 10 years later. It was still the era of the large-scale (by modern standards), five-day annual conference, usually at Eastbourne or Brighton, now supplemented by themed national, one-day conferences – the first was held on housing in London in 1967 and a second on gypsies and other travellers the following year.

Public health departments had evolved into a fairly uniform format, the main divisions of which were food (including meat inspection), offices, shops, clean air and housing. Two new developments in the 1960s were the introduction of meat inspectors, working in abattoirs and reporting to public health departments and the appearance in often over-stretched departments of the technical officer.

The Factories Act of 1961 and the Offices, Shops and Railway Premises Act of 1963 gave new work to departments, laying down, for example, prescriptive or minimum standards on temperature and the provision of washbasins and toilets in the workplace. In 1965, APHI's General Council launched a new venture – an annual report on environmental health – as 'a means of giving factual information on the work carried out by public health inspectors during the year'. Covering England, Wales and Northern Ireland, the reports were based on questionnaires filled in by chief public health inspectors.

On the national stage, the new government's acceptance of the Robbins report in 1964 led to the conversion of colleges of advanced technology into 'red brick universities', an important expansion of higher education. Birmingham's college of advanced technology, which was to become the University of Aston, instituted a four-year degree sandwich course in environmental health. The first environmental health degrees were awarded in 1968. The University of Salford was the next institution to offer one.

The main route to qualification in environmental health was still the diploma. This required passes in at least four GCE 'O' levels (raised to five in 1968) and involved working as a student public health inspector with a local authority (virtually all authorities offered places), combined with a four-year day or block-release course at a technical college. There was a final examination, consisting of five papers, practical examinations on an environmental subject and food and an interview. The minimum age of a diploma-holder was 21. An APHI report on the training and duties of public health inspectors in 1967 revealed that a young, newly-qualified inspector might expect to earn from £1,020 to £1,665 a year, with a transferrable superannuation scheme – more in London. Chief inspectors could earn £2,850 a year or more.

English local government was two-tier. Under counties, which did not employ public health inspectors, were a mixture of sub-administrations, including municipal boroughs, county boroughs, rural districts and urban districts. In the middle of the decade, London local government was restyled – an amalgamation created 31 boroughs beneath a strategic London County Council.

Change was afoot – modernisation was to sweep through all areas of public life. A Royal Commission was set up in 1966 by Harold Wilson, under the chairmanship of Lord Redcliffe-Maud, to consider the structure of local government in England, outside London. Its final main recommendation was for a streamlined system of unitary local government based on larger towns. However, as we shall see in the next chapter, the Conservatives, who came to power in 1970, rejected this proposal in favour of a more complex structure. There was to be no unitary map of local government and some functions that had traditionally sat alongside each other, including environmental health and trading standards, were

Lord Redcliffe-Maud (left) explains his blueprint for local government

split between districts and counties.

An inquiry was going on, in parallel, into the health and welfare services provided by the NHS and local government, which had run along separate lines since the birth of the NHS in 1948. This led, in 1968, to a Department of Health green paper on England and Wales. The green paper appeared at the same time as the Seebohm Report on local authority and allied social services. In 1969, delegates at the association's annual conference must have listened intently to keynote speaker Richard Crossman, head of Labour's new health and social security 'super department', for signs of what was to come.

In this area, the incoming Conservative government of 1970 would largely follow the green paper and the Seebohm Report. Under the Social Services Act of that year, councils' former children's and welfare departments would be scrapped and replaced by new social services departments. Regional and area health authorities would be created for the NHS, except in Wales, where there were only to be area authorities. Medical officers of health would transfer to the health authorities, breaking a link with local government that had lasted for more than 100 years.

For those association members who had called for an end to departments 'working under the general direction' of medical officers of health throughout the 1960s, this was greeted as good news. They had long-argued that the infamous 'general direction' led to too much prescription in their work and blocked career paths, inevitably leaving the top job to a medic.

The structural changes that came on the scene from the end of the 1960s in local government can be seen as a paradigm shift. Health was out, the environment was in. In 1970, the high-profile Royal Commission on Environmental Pollution would be set up to advise the government on environmental issues. It would consider controversial topics, including nuclear power, climate change, the environmental impact of new housing and organophosphates in pesticides. It was closed in 2011 – a victim of the government's spending cuts and its declining interest in green issues.

As the 1960s progressed and environmentalism became a social and cultural imperative, the Association followed suit. In 1969, it re-christened its journal *Environmental Health* and in January 1970, to kick-off European conservation year, it hosted a one-day conference in London called 'The assault on the environment'. Five years later, the professional body would refashion itself as the Environmental Health Officers Association.

In the next decades, environmental concerns that were far more sophisticated and wide-ranging than controlling black smoke would come to the fore, and European regulations and directives painstakingly transposed into UK law would provide the statutory underpinnings of the profession. We can see glimmerings of these developments and echoes of important controversies in the Association's professional journal from the late-1960s. Times were changing. There were even some inspectors – for example, the brave new breed of the Public Health Inspectors London Action Group, or Philag – who listened to jazz and let their hair grow over their collars.

Peculiar to the south of England (radicalism had never died out in the north), Philag members criticised the old guard and campaigned on housing, food and other matters. They were impatient of the Association's slowly grinding gears. They sought a professional body that was more radical and politically-engaged. Many of them were later to assume prominent positions in local government, government departments and the Association itself.

Philag members (radical London health inspectors) shook things up

The pupil inspectors

Alan Higgins, past president and chairman of the CIEH, writes: "I began my career in local government in late 1967 as an administrative trainee with the London Borough of Greenwich. I spent the first year moving around departments, learning about local government, during which time I spent some weeks with the public health inspectors. It was at this point that I decided that I wanted to be an inspector myself, for the variety of work, the independence involved and the fact that I would be doing important work to protect people and improve their lives. The salary looked reasonable, too!

"At the end of the year, I was offered the opportunity to train as a weights and measures inspector (trading standards officers came later), as Greenwich had a vacancy. I stuck to my original intention, in spite of some pressure, and had to spend a year as a clerical assistant in the health and social services department, which was responsible for all social services and health matters including public health.

"I spent the next year dealing with National Assistance burials and clerking for the public health inspectors – a useful grounding for my future profession. The inspectors made hand-written notes and my main job was to transfer them to a property-based card system – no computers in those days! Letters were all typed on typewriters with carbon paper for the file copies – fiddly and pretty poor quality.

"I trained as a PHI at South East London Technical College, doing a three-year sandwich course. Greenwich paid me a salary and I worked in the public health department, doing the fetch-and-carry work for the inspectors – collecting and delivering sample pots, helping on drainage jobs, doing some limited inspection work and working as a meat inspector in the local abattoir. As part of my support, Greenwich paid my membership of the Association of Public Health Inspectors.

"At the end of the course, I was fortunate enough to be nominated for the student medal interviews. These took place in London at the APHI HQ in Grosvenor Place – a very impressive building, although APHI only occupied a small space. It was an extremely hot summer's day and there was a transport strike. I had to walk several miles to the interview, which, I am convinced, resulted in me not winning a medal!

"I took up my post as a PHI in 1972 and I was responsible for a multi-ethnic district in Plumstead in Greenwich. Those early years taught me an amazing amount, as I had complete responsibility for my area, although I was well-supported by older colleagues, many of whom had given up being plumbers to become PHIs and were happy to share their knowledge with a green inspector. Highlights of this period included dealing with a typhoid case whose family worked in a dairy-packing plant, closing a butcher who fed more meat to the rats than his customers and resolving a major drainage problem affecting about 90 properties. You had to learn quickly!

"I also became involved in the South London branch of the Environmental Health Officers Association (EHOA), the successor to the APHI, becoming secretary. Many of the events we organised were similar to work done by branches and regions today, although there was more emphasis on social events. The late 1960s saw the advent of Philag, a group of young London inspectors (mainly male), campaigning to reform their professional body, which they regarded as rather staid and conservative. It was a good time to work in public health, with lots of individual autonomy and a real opportunity to make a difference without much of the bureaucracy that we seem to be burdened with today."

David Purchon, past president of the CIEH, also recalls working his way up from the lowest rung. He recalls: "I joined the world of public health in the 1960s. Disappointed with my first proper job in what is now a nationalised (failed) bank, I became a pupil PHI with Leeds County Borough Council.

"The new language and environment in the sanitation section of the public health department was a shock to the system for a grammar school boy who had been in the sixth form studying English, history and geography, with strange references to common lodging houses, slum-clearance, pest infestations, drainage, meat inspection and sanitation. Our inspectors talked of obscure regulations, standards of fitness, public inquiries, legal notices, works in default and the complexities of sampling. In Leeds, there were 20 pupils, five for each year of a four-year sandwich course. The majority of work seemed to comprise domestic sanitation in privately-rented accommodation.

"There seemed little prospect of the brave new world of 'environmental health' that we would know later, but things were changing rapidly. Clean air was a popular aspiration and someone had to tackle implementation of the Clean Air Act. People aspired to warm, dry homes, which they wanted to own – homes equipped not only with internal bathrooms but with appliances such as refrigerators, washing machines and televisions. The 'window on the world' of television showed them what was possible, particularly in the US, and it became demanded in a nation that, as Harold Macmillan had said a little earlier, had 'never had it so good'.

"The National Society for Clean Air was a powerful influence in the 1960s – how sad that it met its end in 2012, having tried to modernise and become Environmental Protection (UK). Our chief in Leeds was a prominent figure in the NSCA and we had an impressive smoke control programme. The city was dominated by smoking industrial chimneys from its many factories, foundries and workshops. Smoke, grit and dust seemed to be good things to control – hence this young arts-educated inspector's interests turning to combustion engineering. That led to interests in industrial and occupational health and safety, waste management, and in public health engineering generally.

"New legislation was introduced, often in response to press coverage of some perceived scandal involving pollution. It focused attention on the environment, and the need to control noise pollution and emissions to air and water of toxins, asthmagens and pesticides. The newly titled environmental health officers (EHOs) would become familiar with decibels and microgrammes of heavy metals and polyaromatic hydrocarbons – miniscule particles and chemicals that persisted in the environment – and so on.

"In 1974, the Control of Pollution Act drew many environmental controls together and the Health and Safety at Work etc Act introduced a completely new approach to managing occupational health and safety. The EHOs of the 1970s had a new world to occupy, no longer merely inspecting and enforcing but taking an interest in policy, strategy and programming, seeking to manage issues and improve public health. I had had the best of times as an EHP in local government. My involvement continues in the 21st century, now as a consultant and commentator."

Brian Hanna, also a past president, was another of the 1960s intake who was to go on to achieve great things. He achieved the influential position of chief executive of Belfast City Council before his retirement. He recalls: "I qualified as a public health inspector in 1965, having spent four years as a pupil PHI in Belfast City Council's health department while studying part-time at Belfast College of Technology. I had joined the council to pursue a career in finance and administration but a happy sequence of events led me inexorably into the career which has been such a blessing and to which I owe so much. In a sense I didn't choose environmental health, it chose me.

"For almost three decades I worked as an EHO, rising eventually to the position of director in the environmental health department in 1984. I had worked in virtually all areas of environmental health and, as director, I wrongly assumed that I had reached my zenith as far as local government was concerned.

"The work of EHOs in Belfast was extremely difficult in those days, coinciding as it did with the civil disorder which was a daily part of all our lives. I have the highest regard for all the EHOs in Belfast who, without exception, remained true to their professional motto, *amicus humani generis*, thus making a significant contribution to the health and wellbeing of all their fellow citizens."

In the 1960s, John Tiffney, who was to be the profession's president from 1991 to 1993, was a rookie district inspector in south London. Like policemen, PHIs used to walk their beats. He recalls: "When I qualified as a public health inspector in 1963, I was given a district in the Borough of Lambeth. Being keen, I got through a lot of visits and was soon taken to one side and told to slow down as I was making it look bad for the older inspectors! That was before Lambeth had appointed its first chief EHO – the boss was the medical officer of health, who had no enthusiasm for management.

John Tiffney, 'rookie district inspector' in the 1960s, served as president in 1991

"I now recognise that the demise of the MoH and the emergence in the 1970s of EHOs with management expertise was one of the major factors in the development of the profession. I thoroughly enjoyed the multiplicity of tasks and meat inspection in particular (my father was a butcher), and was very aggrieved when LAs lost their meat responsibility in the 1990s.

"I am very proud to have been involved with the development of the CIEH over the past 30 years, especially the acquisition of Chadwick House in 1984, the granting of the Royal Charter and being a signatory to the launch of the International Federation of Environmental Health. I'm privileged to have worked alongside many very able and farsighted colleagues on the General Council. Making friends from the UK and overseas was a bonus, which came as a result of making the effort to get involved in branch, centre and international activities."

Food safety

Food production was more local than today in the 1960s. Throughout the 20th-century, inspectors had been particularly concerned with dairies, abattoirs and backstreet premises producing products such as ice cream, sausages, pies and potted or pickled foods, often without the benefit of refrigeration or wash-basins. The Food Hygiene Regulations of 1955, which still governed their work, had widened the range of premises that were inspected and imposed tougher legal requirements on cleanliness, but there was still no national system of risk-rating. There were no improvement notices, codes of practice were in their infancy and systematic certificated training for food handlers was regarded as a novel concept.

Prominent in the food safety function exercised by local government were the identification, seizure and condemnation of unfit food, using protocols going back to the 1875 Public Health Act. Previously, only public health inspectors and medical officers of health had had powers to seize and condemn unfit meat. New meat inspection regulations introduced in 1960 by MAFF paved the way for similarly empowered meat inspectors, qualified with certificates in meat inspection from the Royal Society of Health. The Association was involved in the creation of the new inspectors. It lobbied for making meat inspection at abattoirs compulsory. This came about in 1963.

Robert Morton, working in north London in the 1960s, recalls seizing contaminated food from a café close to Tottenham Hotspurs' football stadium: "I returned to the health department with a car boot full of rotting food and a full notebook in my pocket and presented myself to my chief EHO, asking where the nearest magistrate was to get the food condemned. He looked up at me then up at the ceiling and said 'God, I need a bible'. I thought it was to pray for deliverance from someone like me. But actually it was for me to swear on when I faced the magistrate. The magistrate signed the order without even looking at the food, let alone listening to my formalities. I became a regular visitor."

Inspecting carcas ses in abattoirs was a routine part of the public health inspector's job in the 1960s

In this era of typewriters, telexes and telephones, communication was far slower than today. Douglas McMurray remembers a serious outbreak of food poisoning in Chesterfield that affected hundreds of people and caused three deaths. The incident led to an early multi-authority epidemiological investigation. The outbreak, it was discovered, was caused by Salmonella typhimurium, which was uncommon in England. The infection was traced to a farm in Yorkshire that was using pigswill from an RAF station, the crews of which made frequent trips to Australia where the phage type was common. The case contributed to a further innovation – training for food handlers. "With Michael Globe, I devised a series of food hygiene courses held all over the district with the title, 'Your health in whose hands?' A thousand food handlers were reached."

A celebrated large-scale food poisoning outbreak of the 1960s produced shocking national headlines. The typhoid epidemic that swept across Aberdeen in May and June 1964 seemed to recall epidemics of the 19th century. Customers who had purchased large tins of corned beef from the town's first supermarket in Union Street became ill. The city's hospital was soon overrun with sufferers – most spent at least four weeks in hospital and were quarantined. More than 500 people were affected. Fortunately, none died. The subsequent Milne enquiry found that during their cooling in Argentina, cans had been contaminated by water from a river polluted with human excrement.

The enquiry found that meat from the same plant had caused typhoid in Harlow, South Shields and Bedford the previous year. MAFF's technical adviser was sent to South America to inspect canning factories. But MAFF, keen to avoid bad publicity, did not act decisively for fear of offending the Argentinian government. Medical officers of health were also kept in the dark by the Department of Health.

An editorial in the July 1964 issue of *The Sanitarian* notes that corned beef is a popular food item and that about 100 cases of typhoid are recorded in the UK each year. This has been the most serious outbreak since 1937. The editorial stresses the need for health education and the vital importance of hand-washing: "Modern premises and new equipment will be of no value if the individual is careless in his personal methods and hygiene." It notes that Aberdeen's overcrowded housing with 65,000 families living in one, two or three-room homes and sharing WCs would have made the disease spread more quickly.

PC Oxley, in Manchester, recalls being involved in removing suspect corned beef from the food chain, soon after the first cases of typhoid were diagnosed in May 1964. He remembers the urgency of what must have seemed like a life-or-death mission: "On 20 May, the first cases of corned beef-related typhoid were registered in the UK, triggering an across-the-nation search for contaminated cans. Only the 4lb and 7lb cans would be suspect, so this narrowed the field. Armed with copies of the consignment numbers embossed on the cans, we set up urgent day and night inspections across the city of retail outlets." Visits were made to grocery shops, cafés, restaurants, hotels, supermarkets, canteens, pubs, night clubs and railway buffets. The sought-after cans were surrendered.

Avocado bravado

Another of the 1960s intake who, unusually, achieved a high-profile role on the commercial side of environmental health was Alan Lacey. Born and bred in the East End of London, Alan went straight into environmental health from East Ham Grammar School in the 1960s.

He explains: "I was a student with the old Stepney Metropolitan Borough Council. After a couple of years, I got the opportunity to specialise in food. I was dealing with the larger food manufacturers and a lot of imported food as there were still warehouses and wharves along the Thames in those days. We also had Spitalfields fruit and veg market."

Supermarkets were smaller than now and did not sell much fresh produce

He says: "In those days, tastes in food were relatively unsophisticated. Supermarkets were far smaller than today. They did not sell much fresh produce or ready-meals. This is making me sound ancient but I can remember the first avocado pears coming into the office and there being great amusement as to what they were. I tasted one and I thought: 'This is awful. Why would anyone want to eat this?' I saw recently that Marks and Spencer had a complaint at the time from a customer who cooked avocado pears and served them with custard."

In the early 1970s, Alan worked with Kent County Council as assistant county health officer. He spent almost 20 years as principal EHO at Wandsworth, with a stint advising the NHS on food hygiene. He first joined Sainsbury's as a food safety advisor in 1995. At that time, it was Britain's number one supermarket.

He recalls: "I had found the slow pace of local government frustrating. I had always been interested in working for the private sector and I am pleased that I made the move. I found out very quickly that you were given a job to do, with lots of responsibility, but you were allowed to get on and do it. It was quite scary at first. But it was exciting."

BSE and genetic modification were emerging as issues and Alan was soon given responsibility for technical public relations, a job he enjoyed very much. As head of regulatory affairs for Sainsbury's from 2003, he was one of the most high-profile private sector EHOs, at a time when many local authority practitioners had a prejudice against companies and regarded this career path as 'the dark side'.

He recalls: "There was a lot of misunderstanding in those days and a 'them and us' attitude was common. I don't know anybody in a large national company who wasn't frustrated by inconsistency and fragmentation in local government enforcement. For example, EHOs would demand copies of our food safety plan as though we had never heard of hazard analysis principles, even though we had a home authority and employed a world-renowned microbiologist who wrote textbooks."

Frustrated, Alan, who had been active in the commercial and industrial centre of the CIEH lobbied for an approach to enforcement that would be more tailored to acknowledge the compliance systems of large food retailers. It helped when Sir Philip Hampton, chairman of Sainsbury's, was commissioned by chancellor Gordon Brown to produce a report on simplifying regulation in 2004. The report was to lead to the creation of the Local Better Regulation Office and a statutory system of primary authorities to co-ordinate enforcement activities for companies on more than one site from 2008.

Alan who is a director and vice chair of the Society of Food Hygiene and Technology left Sainsbury's in 2012 to move to Asda and is also a member of the Better Regulation Delivery Office (BRDO) business reference panel.

He comments: "An awful lot has changed. Looking along the shelves now, we can buy things which were unimaginable in the 1960s. There's a huge range of fresh, healthy foods in supermarkets, the best of which have embraced sustainability, and people have a desire to experiment. The riverside warehouses where I inspected imported foods have been converted to luxury apartments. Consumers have a wider choice of good, safe food than ever before."

Exhumations

Inspectors were occasionally required to perform duties in relation to exhumations from cemeteries. PC Oxley has a sombre recollection of this topic. He writes: "During the early-1960s, a project was undertaken to exhume some 300 human remains from the St Phillips Church graveyard in Manchester's city centre for re-interment at the city's southern cemetery in Chorlton. The graveyard's burial period had included Manchester's cholera epidemic of 1835. Body remains, together with breastplates, a lead casket, pewter artefacts and carpenters' tools, were in large pine boxes for reburial. Coffin boards and wooden fragments were sent for incineration.

"Inspectors worked on a rota. Their duty was to ensure due dignity and security, and to record what evidence they could from inscriptions found on breastplates. Lime dressing was applied to the excavated soil to protect them from infection. The work continued for several months."

PC Oxley was involved in a gruesome exhumation in Manchester city centre

Housing

Primitive housing conditions, including lack of gas, water or electricity supplies, and primitive sanitation, were still common in the 1960s. BS Boulter, working in Northampton, remembers: "Some cities and towns would still have isolated pockets of housing without mains water. One example was a cluster of cottages in Rothersthorpe Road where the water was supplied from a shallow private well… routine sampling revealed the water to be contaminated with matter of animal origin. One elderly lady claimed she had used the water for as long as she could remember without any detrimental effects… A combination of informal and statutory action under the Public Health Act 1936 eventually won the day, triggering a financial contribution from the council."

Housing legislation, most recently from 1957, focused primarily on the large-scale slum clearance of properties deemed unfit and, if necessary, compulsorily purchased. This work continued until the 1970s, when home improvement, local regeneration and 'enveloping' came into vogue.

Gary McGrogan, later director of environment and regulatory services in Sheffield, observes: "In the 1960s, local authorities were required to inspect dwellings within their area to determine whether they were fit for human habitation. Houses that had a low ceiling height, poor ventilation, poor water supply or inadequate drainage were determined to be unfit. The local authority was then required to place a demolition order on the property or, in some cases, a closing order with an undertaking from the owners that they would make the property fit. People were then usually rehoused on newly-built council housing estates."

He adds that many of the unfit houses were abandoned and fell into dilapidation: "Over a decade later, in the 1970s and 1980s, there was a desire to get these properties back into use, with the aid of improvement grants."

In the 1960s, acres of streets in many cities were bulldozed, leaving fields of rubble. PC Oxley remembers a Manchester inspection card, designed by former president of the Institute of Environmental Health Officers, John Graham, that detailed more than 400 points of detail on the unfitness criteria: "Many thousands of pre-1911 houses were inspected in this way by our private sector survey team. The designated areas for clearance, some of the largest in the country, included between 1,000 and 3,000 houses at a time, culminating in upwards of 100,000 unfit houses being cleared in the city, with not a case lost."

The exploitation and harassment of tenants by landlords – Rachmanism – did not magically end at the turn of the decade. Distressingly, it continued. Robert Morton was working as a district EHO on Rachman's patch (Paddington) in the 1960s. Rachman was to be implicated in the Profumo scandal of 1963. He died the year before, having created a West London empire of more than 100 mansion blocks and several nightclubs.

Mr Morton clearly remembers the tricks and 'terror tactics' used by Rachman and similar landlords in Paddington to remove protected tenants and maximise rental income. Properties would be transferred to new companies at the last minute and unpleasant items posted through tenants' letterboxes: "One of the less unpleasant, believe it or not, was a variety of snakes, lizards and frogs. The elderly tenant managed to collect some of them in a biscuit tin to show me. I suspect her landlord had acquired them from a local pet shop. She had originally complained that she had a snake infestation in her flat... Our environmental health offices were also, from time to time, the subject of similar letterbox treatment. Twice we received a firebomb. The second one was very effective on the inside but showed nothing on the outside of the building."

Far from West London, with its shebeens and colourful night life, Neil Scott was working in suburban Henley-on-Thames. It had an affluent reputation, but, as he discovered, life was not all about regattas and strawberries. He quickly identified large numbers of sub-standard properties.

"My main concern was for the tenants, who could do little to improve their lot… at that time, local authorities had no relevant enforcement powers. My frustration was eased in 1964 by legislation enabling local authorities to compel owners to improve tenanted properties, thereby providing them with a hot water supply, a fixed bath or shower, a wash-basin, an inside lavatory and a proper food store – where these were requested… the improvement of tenanted properties throughout the borough was soon underway."

The last two years of the decade saw an important white paper, *Old Houses Into New Homes*, and a piece of legislation from the dying Labour administration that would define housing work in the next decade. *The Sanitarian* of September 1969 notes that 4.5 million homes in the UK are in need of additional facilities or major repair, and that millions of households have no hot water for their bath or sink. It adds: "Only 80,000 are being dealt with each year and the introduction of powers of compulsory improvement in 1964 did little to accelerate this rate."

The journal predicts that, through improvement areas and grants, the 1969 Housing Act will lead to better homes and also car parking, play spaces and street furniture. It could also be linked to smoke control and noise enforcement. *The Sanitarian* urges public health inspectors to get to grips with the act and to play a full part in its implementation.

Caravans and longboats

Not everybody lives in a house. The remit of public health inspectors also covered non-traditional accommodation – bedsits, common lodging houses, hostels and narrowboats. In Manchester, Graham Butterworth had an unusual job: in the 1960s, he was the city's last designated canal boat inspector.

The work kept him busy. He explains: "Constructed for bulk transport of commercial loads, these craft also contained living facilities for the families of

Arthur Harrison, public health inspector, checks a narrowboat for safety and sanitation

the operators or crews. The accommodation usually provided a home for a family, consisting of bunks, a stove for cooking and heating and storage space, all in a confined cabin. The layout frequently resulted in gross contamination, foul air, cross-infection, speedy putrefaction of food and minimal opportunity for personal hygiene."

Although canal boat populations were declining dramatically, the needs of those in another form of non-traditional accommodation remained. For the first time, legislation in 1968 required councils to make provision for a significant section of the caravan-dwelling community: gypsies and, in the words of the act, 'other persons of nomadic habit'.

Terry Oliver, who worked in Surrey, spent a lot of time, like many public health inspectors, bringing caravan sites up to speed. He recalls: "For the size of the district, Chertsey had a very large caravan population, with several sites established during the war years numbering more than 100 vans. Living conditions on these sites improved once they were licensed under the Caravan Sites Act. As a result, over several years, smaller and often insanitary vans were gradually replaced by larger, fully-equipped mobile homes on mains drainage. Suitable roads with street lighting were provided on the larger sites."

Aberfan

In 1966, an economically unstable UK was beset by strikes. In a snap election, Harold 'the pound in your pocket' Wilson consolidated his fragile hold on power. The year was marked by triumph and a tragedy. In July, England won the World Cup. In October, heavy rain caused a mountain of spoil from the Merthyr Vale Colliery to slide onto terraced houses and a primary school in the village of Aberfan.

By the next day, 2,000 emergency workers and volunteers were on the scene. The heart-breaking tragedy stopped the country in its tracks. The landslide led to the deaths of 116 children and 28 adults. It precipitated an inquiry, led by Lord Justice Edmund Davies, that laid the blame on the National Coal Board.

Public health inspector Leonard Griffiths was directly involved and vividly remembers his role following the disaster. He had just completed his training at the Welsh College of Advanced Technology in Cardiff and was working as a district inspector in the County Borough of Merthyr Tydfil.

Mr Griffiths recalls: "On 22 October, 1966, at about 9.20am, a telephone call to our office told us that the village school in Aberfan had been engulfed by colliery spoil, which had been tipped on the side of the valley above the school. The mining waste had been amassed over 50 years and took the form of two black pyramids… Public health department staff had previously routinely visited the school building to check air pollution monitoring equipment located on the roof.

"In the days that followed the disaster, our public health role was conducted from a Gas Board showroom in the village, which had been cleared and occupied by representatives of each of the local authority services and public utilities. Basically, there was a desk and telephone for each service. This proved to be ideal since whatever issue arose, there were people in that one room who, more than likely, could facilitate a solution.

"Our public health role varied from dealing with infestations at temporary dormitories used by volunteers, monitoring public drinking water supplies, working with a group of soldiers to unblock sewers and drains and other duties, liaising with the Salvation Army and Red Cross, which manned feeding stations, and mortuary work. After a few days, there was public concern about the spread of disease because of blocked drains and road gullies. This was a concern not shared by public health staff. However, I arranged for a gallon of phenolic disinfectant to be put in every road gully tanker with 1,200 gallons of water and sprayed over every gully and channel. Although of doubtful public health merit, the public was reassured by the clean disinfectant odour. A lesson learned.

"I have not mentioned the tragic incident itself. At the time, that was something I personally could not dwell on. Like others, we were trying to do our best."

Aberfan landslide – heart-breaking tragedy which stopped the country in its tracks in October 1966

Chronology 1960s

1960

■ Park Hill Estate in Sheffield. The UK's first deck access block. Designed by Sheffield council architects.

■ Labour conference at Scarborough calls for unilateral nuclear disarmament.

■ Noise Abatement Act.

1961

■ Parker Morris report commissioned by Harold Macmillan as he reduces council house standards. Defines minimum space requirements. Mandatory until 1981.

■ Housing minister Keith Joseph, invests £25m in a pilot housing association project.

■ Factories Act. Rationalises legislation.

1962

July Macmillan sacks seven of his cabinet in a 'night of the long knives'. *Mac the Knife* is number one in the pop charts.

■ Last UK outbreak of smallpox, in the Rhondda Valley, South Wales, kills 20 people.

1963

June Minister for war, John Profumo, forced to resign.

October Macmillan quits. Sir Alec Douglas-Home is Prime Minster.

■ National Building Agency advises government on building techniques.

■ Offices, Shops and Railway Premises Act, covering health, safety and welfare of staff, amends the Factories Act 1961.

■ Housing Act (implemented by Labour) sets up the Housing Corporation to fund housing associations.

■ Buchanan Report, *Traffic in Towns*.

1964

October Harold Wilson takes office for Labour.

■ Wilson tells housing and local government minister Richard Crossman: "On housing we win or lose." Target of 400,000 homes per year.

■ Housing white paper. Compulsory improvement grants and strengthened powers on houses in multiple occupation.

■ Protection from Eviction Act.

■ Aberdeen typhoid outbreak.

1965

January Winston Churchill dies.

■ Swingeing spending cuts.

■ Rent Act. Fair rents set by rent officers. Security of tenure under certain conditions.

■ London County Council replaced by the Greater London Council. It is the largest local authority in Europe.

■ Race Relations Act. Milner Holland Report on housing and race.

■ Child Poverty Action Group.

■ TV tobacco advertising banned.

1966

April Wilson wins election. Pledges 500,000 houses to be built per year. Increases in pensions, benefits and tax. Wage and price freeze. Poor industrial relations.

■ England wins World Cup.

■ Aberfan coal tip disaster.

■ TV drama *Cathy Come Home*. Charity Shelter begins.

■ Ministry of Social Security.

1967

March *Torrey Canyon* oil spill.

October Foot and mouth disease outbreak.

November Currency devalued. Average income tax rises from 10 to 14 per cent.

■ Housing Subsidies Act. Housing cost yardsticks to reduce costs. Abolition of the height subsidy.

■ Trellick Tower, in north Kensington designed for the GLC by Erno Goldfinger.

1968

May Ronan Point tower block collapse. More than 10,000 dwellings built after 1970 are demolished within 15 years because of building defects.

July Sterling crisis. Prescription charges re-introduced.

■ Richard Crossman heads Department of Health and Social Security (DHSS).

■ Town and Country Planning Act.

■ Housing white paper shifts emphasis from new-build to renovation.

■ Caravan Sites Act. Restricts eviction from caravan sites and provides new sites.

1969

August. British troops sent to Ulster.

■ Use of Parker Morris standards a condition of receiving housing subsidy. Matching dimensions produces visually monotonous blocks.

■ Housing Act creates general improvement areas. New grants for home improvement and laws on houses in multiple occupation.

■ Circular 82/69 creates category one and two sheltered housing.

The 1970s

The party's
over

Nobody expected Edward Heath to win the 1970 general election – not even Edward Heath. Labour had been ahead in the polls, the weather was good and – the pound having been devalued in 1968 – the balance of trade was in the black. The election was held in June. Mr Heath, mocked as 'Selsdon man' by Labour because he had held a pre-election meeting in the unforgivably suburban Selsdon Park Hotel in Croydon, romped home by 30 seats and found himself in Downing Street. Like Harold Wilson, he was a grammar school boy – not a representative of the traditional ruling classes.

One of Mr Heath's assets was to be the brand new Department of the Environment. A concrete and glass vision of the future, it was located in three, 20-storey concrete towers that were soon labelled 'the ugly sisters' and 'the toast rack' (they were demolished in 2003). A new 'super department', the DoE was a merger of the Ministry for Housing and Local Government and the Ministry of Transport. The department had a £14bn budget and 50,000 staff. As well as running local government, housing, planning and transport, it would be responsible for the concerns about environmental quality that had

The Department of the Environment was housed, in 1970, in 'the ugly sisters'

come to the fore in the 1960s and was to provide the main focus for lobbying from the Association of Public Health Inspectors and its successors until the 1990s.

Peter Walker, at its head, was something of a maverick – a former business tycoon, who had headed asset strippers Slater Walker, who had not gone to university and who drove an E-type Jaguar. He was to be in charge of the local government re-organisation, following the Redcliffe-Maude report of 1969. It was Conservative policy that two-tier local government would be retained and Mr Walker looked at Labour's proposals with fresh eyes.

The Local Government Act of 1972, implemented in 1974, was the first large-scale change to local government since 1888. Changes to the NHS, transferring medical officers of health from councils to health authorities, were implemented at the same time. The measures had major repercussions for environmental health. Globally, the number of councils was hugely reduced – down from 1,400 outside London to only 422. Most controversially, the act retained a two-tier structure for southern England, with 333 districts (including former rural and urban districts and county boroughs) sitting beneath 47 counties. In the two-tier areas, environmental health, like housing and planning, was to become a district function. Trading standards would join social services, highways and waste disposal at county hall. In 1972, local government had lost water responsibilities to public sector water authorities.

In the generally Labour-controlled North, the act created unitary metropolitan district and borough councils that would run all services. There were also six new large strategic authorities, including Greater Manchester and Merseyside. These would be abolished, along with the Greater London Council, in 1986. To make councils sound more business-like, their most senior paid officials would now be called 'chief executives' – no more town clerks. Wales would also have a primarily two-tier system. In Northern Ireland, following a good deal of deliberation, the existing districts, excluding Belfast, would be formed into groups. Each group would have specialists and a chief inspector.

During the bill's second reading, Mr Walker had said: "I decided that environmental health was best dealt with at district level. This will enable districts to employ public health inspectors who can continue to carry out the range of functions which honourable members will agree they have carried out exceedingly well in the past."

The General Council of the Association of Public Health Inspectors was split. It was against some of the changes, particularly the migration of refuse, drug and certain food functions to counties, and the loss of statutory officer status for public health inspectors. But it sensed that they were a fait accompli. Instead of taking an oppositional stance, it decided, in Reg Johnson's words, to "secure acceptance by district councils of the concept of a comprehensive and unified environmental health service, in drawing up their management and department structure". 'General direction' by medical officers of health was gone – removed by the NHS restructuring of the Social Services Act. The future had been set.

In March 1972, the association published a joint memorandum with the Guild of Public Health Inspectors entitled 'The environmental health functions of district councils'. Following proposals contained in the government's Bains Report, it laid down suggestions for duties and departmental structures. Crucially, it suggested, the comprehensive environmental health service of each district, even if it was a sub-division of another department, should be led by a chief environmental health officer.

Viewed in a certain light, things did not seem to be so bad. Mr Johnson observes: "The functions of the PHI had been kept together and the fragmentation which at one time seemed likely had been avoided. Career prospects for members of the profession had been considerably enhanced and the vast majority of chief EHOs had retained their status."

Reflecting the mood of change that was in the air, the Association decided to adopt a new name for itself – the term 'public health' seemed old-fashioned. In November 1974, an extraordinary annual meeting was called in Sutton Coldfield for the purpose. The option chosen, the Environmental Health Officers Association, was approved by the Department of Trade and Industry in 1975.

It was felt that the Guild of Public Health Inspectors, a trade union, was not needed any more, since local government salaries and service conditions were dealt with effectively by Nalgo. But there was a need for a body that would monitor EHOs' terms of employment. In due course, a new Society of Environmental Health Officers was registered as a company and the guild was wound up. The assets of the former Benevolent and Orphans Fund were transferred to a new Environmental Health Officers Welfare Fund.

Dark forces were moving in the world outside. One could even say that the UK was in crisis. Councillors were objecting strongly to the new rates and rent settlement that Peter Walker had attempted to impose by legislation, notably in Clay Cross, Derbyshire, where the councillors' refusal to set a rate was dubbed a 'rebellion'.

Hopes for calmness and consensus that had been associated with 'Selsdon man' had been dashed. By the middle of the decade, the economy was in deep trouble and industrial unrest had set in, including a national miners' strike and power workers' strikes that plunged the country into darkness. Confounding conventional economics, there was 'stagflation' – a combination of inflation and high unemployment. The government imposed a series of three-day weeks. Added to these woes were the 'troubles' in Northern Ireland and a mainland IRA bombing campaign. The Conservatives were also split over Europe. In 1972, the UK joined the European Economic Community – a move given legitimacy by a referendum in 1975.

A general election in February 1974 produced a hung parliament. A re-run in October gave Labour a small majority of three seats. To take the pressure off local government, Labour immediately repealed much of the Housing Finance Act to stop councils' rents from rising (the bone of contention at Clay Cross). Sensing that its hold on power was fragile, Labour, in a brief burst, introduced the Health and Safety at Work and Control of Pollution Acts, and legislation on sexual discrimination and equal pay.

It was the poor state of industrial relations and the economy that would seal Labour's fate. Reg Johnson, author of *A Century of Progress*, takes up the story. He records that by July 1975, only a year after the reorganisation, there was "depression and frustration" throughout local government. He records severe restrictions of expenditure, serious staff shortages and the cutting back of programmes of all kinds. Looking back from 2012, the measures sound familiar. There was an estimated 20 per cent shortage of environmental health staff. Even the finances of the EHOA were stretched. It recorded a deficit of £13,000 at the end of the year, which cut into its reserves.

With councils in mind, Anthony Crosland, Labour's suave, cheroot-smoking education and science secretary, told an audience in Manchester town hall in May 1975 that "the party's over". The following year, the chancellor, Dennis Healey, had to humiliate himself and the country by seeking a crisis loan from the International Monetary Fund. The strictest capital controls for decades were being imposed on local government in the form of standard spending assessments. Spending on housing, a litmus test for governments since the 1950s, was slashed.

Rubbish piled up on the streets in the 'winter of discontent', sealing James Callaghan's fate

Labour limped on for three years as the state of the country worsened. It was buttressed, briefly, by a pact with the Liberal party. Even that went sour: Prime Minister Harold Wilson was convinced that MI5 was plotting his downfall and the pact was rocked when Liberal leader Jeremy Thorpe was placed on trial for conspiracy to murder. The second half of the 1970s was marked by economic turbulence and social unrest – 1978 is remembered as the 'winter of discontent'. To nobody's surprise, James Callaghan, who took over from Mr Wilson in 1976, threw in the towel and called a general election for May 1979. Margaret Thatcher, who had become leader of the Conservatives in 1975, now led her party to a startling victory.

It's easy to forget that, amidst all of the crises, there had been important legislation. In two short periods in government, Labour had liberalised Britain's laws in line with a more tolerant and less stuffy society. Local government and the NHS had both gone through shape-shifting re-organisations. Public health inspectors had been re-christened environmental health officers and de-coupled from medical officers of health. They were working for far fewer councils than previously. Away from the Midlands and the North, the era of a large, powerful public health department reporting to an important council committee was on the wane.

Based on the well-considered template of the 1972 Robens Report, a mass of laws and agencies inherited from the Victorians had been simplified into a new and comprehensive system of health and safety enforcement. The new model, with regulation split between the Health and Safety Commission and Executive and local authorities, was underpinned by a solid piece of legislation, the Health and Safety at Work etc Act of 1974. In housing, the clear and rebuild phase of the 1950s and 1960s had ended. Community-based regeneration was flavour of the decade, with housing associations taking on a greater role. Area improvement was the new buzzword. Mass council house building would not return.

EHOs' traditional employers, local authorities, may be declining but environmental health professionals were better trained and were now finding new roles and employers. Their professional body would recover from the travails of the mid-1970s. In fact, the next decade would be its most successful ever.

One of the most prominent figures of the era in environmental health was Morley Parry, who served as food hygiene officer at the Department of Health and Social Security. Mr Parry, a knowledgeable and popular speaker, was a vice president of the Association. He died prematurely, during the Association's annual conference in Eastbourne in 1973. In 1976, his name was commemorated by an annual award, open to students specialising in food safety.

The association's president in 1977, Eric Wakelin, had achieved prominence in Birmingham as its chief public health and housing inspector. Mr Wakelin created a comprehensive environmental health department – the country's largest. It included cleansing, environmental protection and urban renewal functions, and veterinary and analysts' services. An advisor to the Ministry of Housing and Local Government, he was a pioneer of housing improvement.

He was succeeded as president in 1979 by Mick Archer. Mr Archer, an expert on air pollution, had also been director of

Mick Archer, air pollution expert, a prominent president in the 1970s

Birmingham's environmental health service, including urban renewal, working with the council's chief executive, Jim Amos. He was heavily involved in the creation of the first environmental health degree, at Aston University, and served on the influential Royal Commission on Environmental Pollution from 1981 to 1985.

Student inspectors

David Clapham writes: "It was the best of times… That's it – for me, it was just the best of times. In 1971, I was a student public health inspector for Beeston and Stapleford Urban District Council (which became Broxtowe Council). I would be there for four years, while studying at Trent Polytechnic.

"You did two days at college and three days at work, putting the theory into practice. There was no training plan. You just went on visits with the inspectors you got on with. If you were useful and didn't get in the way, the good ones were happy to take you out. If there was anything interesting, you got included – ratting at the tip, food inspections (walls, floors, ceilings, doors), dealing with noisy neighbours, watching smoky chimneys and, on one occasion, clearing out a cheese shop where the owner had done a midnight flit several months before. Freezer breakdowns were brilliant. Rather than send the semi-thawed food to the tip, if it was still edible, you ate it.

"The professional practice portfolio system consisted of a big sheet of paper. It was full of squares that you ticked against various bits of experience you undertook. On the first morning of every month, it was my job to collect the air pollution bottles from the roof of three schools and take them to the lab. 1973 was the last year we did not get New Year's Day off as a bank holiday. At eight o'clock that morning, I nearly walked straight off a roof carrying a large, rain-filled plastic carboy. It was before the Health and Safety at Work etc Act. I took the afternoon off sick.

"To a young chap like me, most of the complainants seemed odd. There was one woman who locked an inspector in the outhouse to teach him a lesson for 'going around robbing old ladies'. A mother and daughter made a food complaint about pigeons (they had boiled them, roasted them and fried them – but they were still too tough). They told me in answer to the usual question, 'We always have diarrhoea, young man.' There was a house with tinfoil wallpaper to 'keep out the rays from Russia'. One man kept putting his head on the top of the gas fire when you talked to him. He had a metal plate in his head and it hurt when it got cold."

Andy Statham, later a fellow of the CIEH and chairman of the board of trustees, followed a similar route to David Clapham, which, in the 1970s, was a typical one. Leaving school in 1977 with a clutch of 'O' and 'A' levels, he was accepted as a student EHO by Amber Valley DC in Derbyshire, on the vertiginous salary of £70.69 a month (he recalls that, in those days, a pint of bitter cost 20p). The job was based in Ripley under the watchful eye of Barrie Sheard.

Mr Statham recalls: "The nearest diploma course was at Nottingham Trent Polytechnic, a well-established, EHORB-accredited course under the capable tutorage of George Hopper, Alan Crawford and Geoff Plant. Over the next three years, eight fellow course members and I were provided with a superb education by these three lecturers. During term breaks,

Andy Statham shown with air-quality monitoring equipment in Amber Valley

I would return to Amber Valley and engage in practical training with EHOs and technical staff. Having qualified, I secured a district EHO post with Amber Valley and have never looked back since. On reflection the old diploma course provided a superb mixture of theoretical and practical 'on the job' training."

Graham Jukes, later to become the chief executive the CIEH, also recalls being "thrown in at the deep end" and getting more than he bargained for, as an entrant into the profession in the 1970s. He recalls: "I started work in environmental health in 1971 as a junior infectious disease clerk to the medical officer of health, in a west London borough, becoming a student EHO after 15 months. In this role, I spent a considerable amount of time on night surveillance with the inspectors during a precursor to Operation Meathook, which was to shut down abuses in the meat trade, in the 1980s.

"This national meat crime surveillance exercise followed the discovery of imported kangaroo meat and other unfit meat being sold as beef burgers to multiple burger bars and restaurants. The undercover operations that I took part in with the police could have been taken from an episode of *The Sweeney*. They were surreal. At 12.30 one morning, sitting in a blacked out car, I witnessed a white van pull up outside what we observed to be a meat cutting plant, in an alleyway in Fulham.

"The arrival of the mysterious van was to be a regular event in the coming days and nights of recording the comings and goings of an illicit meat trade, supplying restaurants and food outlets throughout the country. The subsequent matching up of the surveillance records against the accounts of the con men, following a joint EHO/police raid, brought about convictions and the closing down of that particular illicit trade. But, over the years, many other food criminals would follow in their footsteps."

Females in a male world

Lynda John qualified as a public health inspector in 1970, after spending four years in college in Cardiff. She was one of the first females to qualify in Wales.

She writes: "My student days started with some hard knocks as I quickly adjusted to life from a strict girls' school to wild college days in a class of 12 boys. On my first day at college, I can remember walking into a room full of strangers, and they were all male. Then, to my relief another girl walked in and we were to become friends for life. We followed a strange and varied curriculum. I was soon to learn about differing subjects from microbiology to building construction and science. Whoever heard of a girl making concrete blocks in those days? Or being able to draw a section through a sliding sash window?

"One of our subjects was meat inspection. Now thankfully, I am not your squeamish type. Whoever invented sex discrimination legislation was probably not born in those days. They were fun times though and the slaughter men spoiled me. There was always liver or sweetbreads for my tea. Although I did not participate in their favourite dish - udder sandwiches! Neither did I eat in their mess room!

"I worked in one abattoir where the owner used to leave their two toddlers in a pushchair watching the slaughtering process, a strange way of babysitting and hard to believe, but true. My mother nearly had a turn when I arrived home from college one day with a plastic bottle full of cat fleas and when she saw bed bugs Sellotaped to my college notes! I was warned: 'Don't you bring those in here!' She used to say that she couldn't understand where I came from. The four years passed quickly and, in 1970, I qualified.

"Unfortunately, there were only five of us females in Wales at the time and getting a job proved difficult, especially as there was no vacancy in Neath where I had trained. I applied for a job in Swansea for which I was unsuccessful because the boss thought I would be 'disruptive to the male staff'. Unbelievable but true! Even when I was a student the boss once told me that I had better not go out on the district on my own in case people would object to a young girl visiting them. My response to that was: 'Hopefully I'll qualify next year and I have no plans for a sex change between now and then!' He never stopped me going out alone again! I eventually got work in Llanelli, where I met my husband. In the days before the M4 it was no mean feat travelling there every day.

"I have spent the last 40 years in the 'life of grime'. It's not for everyone, but I, personally, would not have had it any other way. My college group held their 40-year reunion a few years ago and we are planning to celebrate our 50th. Although our numbers are dwindling, incredibly we're all still friends."

Janet Russell, OBE, who became the CIEH's first woman president in the Diamond Jubilee year, 2012, was also part of the generation who entered the

Janet Russell, Yorkshire EHO and the
CIEH's first female president in 2012

profession in the 1970s. Born in 1956 in Leeds, which is still her home, Janet attended a 'failing' (in her words) inner-city secondary school. Her father had won a scholarship to grammar school, joined the RAF and became manager of an engineering works. His work ethic was an inspiration. Wanting to be a dietician, but lacking a chemistry 'A' level, she took her environmental health diploma in Leeds and qualified as an EHO in July 1977, on the day that the Queen visited Wakefield, the town where she trained. Here, she was one of only two women in an all-male department – the first females to inspect the borough's slaughterhouses.

In 1980, she transferred to work as a district EHO in Castleford, a mining town in Kirklees, to cover for a colleague, Les Dyl, who was touring Australia with Great Britain rugby league team. She recalls: "Castleford was a depressing place due to the thick smog that shrouded it in winter. Buildings developed thin layers of soot and washing was dirtier after it had dried than before it was washed. Naturally, it fell to the newby to do the worst jobs and one of mine was to introduce the first of three smoke control areas to the town.

"Miners would not readily accept my explanation that the two tons of smokeless fuel they would receive were higher in calorific value than the eight tons of concessionary coal they currently received. I had never heard such swearing. But after two years and much heartache, Castleford's number one smoke control area became operational. I don't think I have done anything since that has had such a dramatic impact on quality of life.

"Whilst the wisdom now is to keep communities together, it was different in the 1970s. Clearance on a grand scale was the way. One of the saddest tasks I had was helping with the demolition of Silkstone Row in Altofts, the longest terrace of houses in Europe. Were the houses unfit? Probably not. Did they need repairs – certainly yes. Was it a community? Definitely. I had a real empathy with the residents whose community had been ripped apart.

Ms Russell moved up the managerial tree in Kirklees, becoming a service director and then, in 1999, a divisional director, heading up transport and environment services, building, property services, cleaning and catering. Earlier, she had commissioned from Friends of the Earth the UK's first state of the environment report, which led to the council establishing an Environment Unit in environmental health.

She recalls: "Whilst many viewed it as innovative, some dismissed it as the 'tree hugging department'. These days, environmental work by local authorities is accepted as mainstream but it certainly wasn't then. We dealt with fuel poverty, reducing energy bills on council buildings, supporting community groups and schools and generally putting environmental issues into the heart of council decision-making.

In 2008, in a £20m scheme partly funded by Scottish Power, 80,000 homes in Kirklees were insulated and given carbon monoxide detectors, low-energy light bulbs and energy efficiency advice. The Kirklees Warmzone delivered carbon savings of 55,000 tonnes a year, created 140 jobs and saved £14m for residents. It was the largest scheme of its kind in the country and helped Kirklees to be named council of the year.

In 1998, Ms Russell was appointed to the government's better regulation task force, chaired by Lord Haskins. She notes: "I was the only public sector member. The others were mainly high-flyers from the business world and our office overlooked the garden of 10 Downing Street. I looked around me and I thought, 'this is it. I've made it'. Over the coming months, I'm proud to say that we developed the five principles of better regulation – proportionality, transparency, targeting, accountability and consistency. My environmental health training proved invaluable for engaging with stakeholders, asking searching questions, evaluating information and making recommendations for improvement.

"In 2003, I interviewed Elizabeth Gyngell, head of policy at the Health and Safety Executive. She told me about her goal to set up a service to support those with ill health to get back into work. We now set up the Kirklees Better Health at Work programme. It involved health partners, the HSE, small businesses and GPs, who were repeatedly reviewing patients, but did not have practical ways to help back into work.

"The service is now part-funded and has built up good relationships. It has expanded its work to include mental health issues and to provide healthy workplace advice and training to employers of all sizes. We know it's made a real difference and, looking back, it is something else in my career that I am proud to have been involved with."

Housing

Rodney Dykes recalls how after a particular Lancaster Symposium at the turn of the decade EHOs were sent forth on a mission to improve housing conditions. He says: "As it occurred within days of the passing of the Housing Act 1969, the assembled EHOs were charged with the responsibility of an assault on the circumstances of private sector housing: grant aid for landlords, area-based renewal and regeneration, a new strategic thinking on what was 'fit', and a plethora of secondary advice, not least of which was the famous 82/69 Department of the Environment circular concerning sheltered housing, which for many of us became more than just bedtime reading.

"For me, four years after qualifying from the Royal College of Advanced Technology, Salford, it meant my environmental health role and career were forever changed. I had done blocked drains, full-time meat inspection, food and drugs sampling and endless formal and informal notices under public health and housing legislation. Here came a real opportunity to commit to housing. Within months of Lancaster, I was appointed at a nearby authority, Heywood Metropolitan Borough Council, to concentrate on housing improvement."

Interventions could be made on a city-wide scale. Peter Archer, a past CIEH chairman, writes: "Between 1945 and 1973, Birmingham demolished more than 65,000 homes through slum clearance and redevelopment programmes. In addition, thousands of houses were zoned for future clearance and designated as 'temporary' accommodation under the 1957 Housing Act. These areas of decrepit Victorian houses became known as 'twilight zones'. The word 'temporary' became meaningless, as the redevelopment programme stalled, partly because of a lack of money and partly due to increasing local opposition to the destruction of communities and to moving families to the peripheral council estates.

"Before the 1969 Housing Act, compensation for demolished homes was minimal and normally based on site value. After 1969, the supplement paid to owner-occupiers losing their homes brought the level of compensation to 'market value' and the bill for redevelopment rose steeply. Nationally, the economy had been damaged by the oil crisis, which came to a head in October 1973 when crude oil prices quadrupled over a matter of just a few months.

"By the early-1970s, Birmingham's massive slum clearance programme was winding down and a group of officers and councillors prepared a new 20-year programme of restoration and renewal. An experienced environmental health officer, Reg Bowen, supported by Terry Brunt and Geoff Eden, led the ongoing debate about finding the most effective way of dealing with the remaining 110,000 pre-1919, mainly Victorian homes, many of which were still without the most basic amenities and in substantial disrepair.

"I joined Birmingham's urban renewal programme from West Bromwich on 1 April, 1974 at the point of local government reorganisation. The 1974 Housing Act provided new powers to declare 'housing action area', where there was social and physical deprivation. The newly-formed urban renewal sub-committee established project teams in Small Heath, Sparkbrook, Moseley and Nechells. The multi-disciplinary teams included EHOs, architects, planners, housing officers and social workers.

"The project teams worked through a novel process of full community involvement with residents, businesses, churches, mosques, schools, councillors and the local MPs, all participating in open meetings, workshops and committees. One

Birmingham saw city-wide housing interventions

of our first tasks when arriving in an area was to call people together to form new residents' associations. The aim was to be inclusive when working with a diverse community.

"In the 1960s, more than a third of Sparkbrook residents were immigrants from the Irish Republic, but by the 1970s, Pakistanis from Mirpur had become the predominant ethnic group. Each project team included members from the local communities who could speak Urdu, Punjabi, Arabic and Bengali. Women from the local communities were employed as 'ethnic minority officers' who could interpret and translate publicity into all the locally-spoken languages.

"Within each housing action area, such as Sparkbrook East, residents worked with project team professionals to produce an environmental scheme including home improvement, clearance and environmental improvements such as play areas and new parks. This process often took years rather than months. Members of parliament such as Roy Hattersley and Denis Howell were able to highlight issues of concern with the national press and in parliament.

"In 1979, the concept of 'enveloping' was developed for the twilight areas. Whole streets were renovated externally from the chimney pots to the foundations. Over the next 10 years, around 11,000 inner city homes were renovated in this way. Work proceeded on the basis of a 100 per cent grant, regardless of tenure. Brought to an end in 1989, undoubtedly it was an imaginative and effective way of improving homes and locations.

"Working for urban renewal was exhilarating. We saw an environmental health budget move from £100,000 to £75m, exceeding that of the city's huge housing department. More than 30 years on, the success of the programme is still visible in Birmingham. The city's urban renewal programme remains one of the most ambitious and successful anywhere in Western Europe."

Pests and pitfalls

Public health inspectors were required, at times, to carry out peculiar and difficult duties. Maldwyn Jones, who worked for six local authorities and one supermarket chain recalls: "I struggled all the way through college, but, in 1970, I was the happiest man in the world to have passed and to become a public health inspector – something I have cherished and been proud of. I ended up as a principle EHO in Powys County Borough Council, but I was really much happier being a brave not a chief. I liked the direct contact with Joe Public."

He remembers, in the course of his career, quite a few 'cock-ups', which he is brave enough to admit to and generally learned from. For example, the case of the wasps in the cemetery. He writes: "One of the general duties I had was to assist the pest control team, particularly at times when they were very busy. On this occasion, I was called in to deal with a wasps' nest in a local cemetery.

A domestic pigeon infestation led to a sticky problem EHO Maldwyn Jones

"On arriving , I could see that the very large nest was, in fact, attached to the back of an old concrete headstone. In those days, we used a treatment called multispray. This was petroleum-based insecticide that we sprayed through a pump. If you lit the spray with a match, a flame much like a blow-torch would be created.

"We lit the sprayer and were having great success with destroying the nest, when, all of a sudden, the gravestone broke in half with the top half falling to the ground. It was panic stations, as you can imagine. We determined that the gravestone was very old and we managed to obtain an adhesive compound to stick it back together. I've never been back to check if it's still intact – I'm afraid to do so. I am not, however, disclosing the name of the cemetery.

Then there was the case of the perilous pigeons: "I was in my office one day, when a very weak, elderly lady began crying on the phone, saying that pigeons were roosting on her roof, gutters and window ledges. She was afraid to go out in her backyard and they were cooing day and night.

"Being a newly-qualified inspector, I assured her I would put things right. So I borrowed my brother's air-rifle and went to the lady's house. Sure enough, the pigeons were there, so I shot one of them. The remainder flew off. I was now standing in the middle of the back garden, like John Wayne, waiting for the pigeons to return.

"All of a sudden I could hear the sound of sirens. Before I knew it, I was surrounded by a police armed response team, with guns pointed and visors down. The woman next door had said there was a man in the garden who she didn't know and who was firing a gun.

"I had to lie on the floor with my hands behind my head and throw the gun away. Thankfully one of the police officers recognised me as they were about to cuff me. Apparently, I could have been fined for using an air rifle within so many metres of a public highway anyway. Fortunately they didn't prosecute as I let them keep the gun. I had to buy my brother another one."

Mr Jones rounds off his recollections with a combination of slapstick and black humour. He writes of supervising an exhumation: "It's quite a boring task until you actually reach the coffin. I was standing next to the grave that was being exhumed, leaning up against an adjacent but old, headstone with my notebook in my hand. I was making notes as the dig was progressing. All of a sudden the headstone I was leaning against fell backwards to the ground. I also fell and toppled into the part opened grave. I was covered in mud but I wasn't ready to be buried just yet."

Lynda John, who studied in Cardiff with Maldwyn, also has some colourful memories. One of them is an incident with fleas: "The local authority was improving its housing stock. They were decanting families into other houses whilst the building work was being carried out. I received a phone call, explaining that a particular family had a problem with insects.

"When I arrived at the house with pest control, insects were everywhere. I immediately recognised them as fleas – probably cat fleas from a previous tenant. I caught some fleas in a sample pot to take back to the office and arranged for pest control to deal with the problem.

"As I stood outside the house, the pest control officer shouted: 'Don't get into your car. Look!' He pointed to my legs. I looked down and could see my legs were covered in fleas which seemed to be attached to my tights. I said to him 'just spray me as quick as you can'. There I was in the middle of the street being sprayed with pesticide."

Later, she had to inspect an unlicensed sex shop, which her local authority had decided to prosecute: "One of the male inspectors had to visit the shop and carry out an inventory of the stock, in order to prove that the majority of the items on sale were 'sex articles'. The chief EHO asked him to pick a female officer to accompany him and chose me.

"We spent three days in the sex shop amongst dusty Bay City Rollers records and herbal tablets which were so dirty they left rings around the shelves when you picked them up. The only thing that worried me was that people that I knew would see me going in and out of there. One man came in wearing ripped jeans with fishnet tights underneath them. I have forgotten what he asked me for. I can tell you those three days were an eye-opening experience for me. The statements we wrote were so explicit that the typists wouldn't type them."

Food safety

In 1972, after 20 years in local government, EHO Mike Jacob became senior public health advisor at the Department of Health and Social Security (the 'super department' created in 1968 for Richard Crossman). He was able to bring practical knowledge to the role and help to improve systems. Food was big business now. The job involved liaising between public health departments and food companies to ensure that food safety law was "adequate, effective, fairly administered and transparent".

Early in the job, Mr Jacob was involved in the national withdrawal of a contaminated food product. To his astonishment, the process involved the DHSS sending out thousands of telegrams to medical officers of health, public health laboratories and councils.

He – or someone else – had an idea: the telephone! "There was then an agreement," recalls Mr Jacob, "to introduce a 'cascade' series of telephone calls, whereby one call from the DHSS to each agreed area contact would be passed on using a cascade system."

He adds: "Modern methods have made the cascade system obsolete… The DHSS/LA system, which operated with success for many years, was possible because public health inspectors and their local food companies jointly understood the importance of urgent co-operative action when needed."

Times were changing. Alan Eames notes: "The establishment of supermarkets, multinational companies, chilled and fast foods and ready meals involved complex systems of production and distribution." EHOs needed to move beyond their traditional priorities and develop new concepts in microbiology.

He recalls: "The need was identified by a group of local authority EHOs, the DHSS, the Public Health Laboratory Service and by Dr, subsequently Professor, Ron Board, of the University of Bath."

A microbiology steering group was set up and organised residential courses at the University of Bath. The influential courses, which fully involved the food industry, ran for the next 20 years. They considered how the emerging science of hazard analysis could be applied through the food chain to processes such as chilling, packaging, temperature control, transport and labelling.

Smoke control

James Goss writes: "Early in 1970, I was appointed as a divisional EHO with responsibility for the continued implementation and completion of the smoke control programme under the provisions of the Clean Air Act 1956 in a west London borough.

Emissions to air problems were more complex than the smoke abatement of the 1950s

"In terms of residential occupancies, the smoke control programme was almost complete and the benefits in terms of cleaner air were at last becoming apparent. My task was to make the necessary smoke control orders for the remaining areas where industry was the main problem. The north-east part of the borough contained one of the highest concentrations of industry in London and the South-East. I was advised that there would be very little left to do. I took a different view, as I believed that the true levels of pollution would really be revealed once the smoke had cleared.

"The Public Health (Recurring Nuisances) Act 1969 was about to become operative and I looked forward to using its provisions to address emission problems beyond simple smoke abatement. The elimination of smoke was straightforward, as this could be achieved by improved combustion temperatures or fuel substitution. In formulating the approach to the final smoke control orders, my aim was to determine the full nature of the industrial furnace emissions and to evaluate all associated emissions.

"The industrial areas included a number of heavy metal processes, including nickel refining and lead and alloy production and pressure die-casting of zinc alloys. Metallic emissions included cadmium in addition to less common metals. Following initial visits to discuss the forthcoming smoke control requirements, I began a systematic sampling programme in the vicinity of lead-fume and dust-emission sources. I soon found highly enhanced concentrations of lead on land within a distance of one to two chimney heights from the point source of the chimneys, far in excess of what passed for normal levels in London at that time.

"On one occasion, I explained the significance of sampling results to a managing director in his office overlooking the interior of a lead factory. The exhaust for the lead furnaces discharged above the roof as required but as the large entrance doors were usually left open, some discharge re-entered the premises. I explained that the highest concentration of lead was on the windowsill of his office. He suggested to me that this was perhaps why a succession of guard dogs had died within six months. Later, I observed the sad sight of an empty kennel within the area of highest lead fall out: the water bowl was still in position.

"My work resulted in improvements in four of five lead-processing premises and the removal of two quite large areas of lead-contaminated public parkland. The parkland was reinstated with clean soil at the expense of the emitting premises. Later, a small re-refining operation for high-value heavy metals had to fund the removal and replacement of the rear garden of adjacent residential premises."

Another significant source of atmospheric lead had yet to be tackled – petrol. Awareness of the problem arrived in the late 1960s, but it took 30 years of campaigning before leaded petrol was banned in the UK.

Smoke control work, in the form of implementing smoke control orders, persisted in the Midlands and North well into the 1970s. John Marsh, as head of an environmental health service in the Nottinghamshire coalfield, was responsible for an air-quality black-spot with a strong resistance to smoke control. There were three collieries in his area and thousands of National Coal Board employees, who received 12 tons a year each of concessionary coal. In 1953, a deposit gauge in the centre of the district recorded 15 tons of particulate deposits over a square mile in one month.

Mr Marsh had taken a job in the new Mansfield District Council after the 1974 local government reorganisation. He recalls: "I found that the district had 44,000 dwellings, only 4,000 of which were subject to smoke control orders." He needed to convince the new council of the need for a phased smoke-control programme. This was no easy task since: "I had a new council and the majority of members were employed in the mining industry and my environmental health committee chairman was an official of the National Union of Mineworkers." Against opposition, Mr Marsh introduced volumetric samplers for smoke and sulphur dioxide, finding evidence of levels exceeding Medical Research Council danger thresholds. With the help of a doctor, he established there were high levels of chronic lung conditions in the general community and recorded hospital admissions after episodes of high levels of air pollution.

By late 1974, he was able to present a comprehensive report to the council and a detailed plan for a phased introduction of smoke control across the whole district by 1993. He recalls: "The overall effect of domestic smoke control in the district from 1974 to 1993 was dramatic. By the mid-1980s, buildings were cleaner, painting was lasting much longer and winter sunshine hours increased, so no public transport services were ever suspended due to dense winter smog. By the late-1980s, the council was entering the Britain in Bloom competition and winning awards, and by 1993 our air quality was as good as anywhere in the UK."

Smallpox

Officially, smallpox had been eradicated from the world. The UK's last outbreak of the disease was in the Rhondda Valley, South Wales, in 1962. Brought in by a traveller from Pakistan, it killed 19 people. But stocks of the virus were still held in laboratories. The world's last fatality from the disease tragically affected a medical photographer from the anatomy department of the University of Birmingham Medical School in 1978. Her name was Janet Parker. She accidentally came into contact with a strain of the virus that was being grown in the university's research laboratory. An inquest found lax procedures at the school. Its former head of microbiology later committed suicide.

Janet Parker, a medical photographer, was the last UK victim of smallpox

R Redgate, divisional environmental health manager for Birmingham, was responsible for the area in which she died. He recalls: "We set up a team of three senior officers, comprising me, my opposite number on the other side of Birmingham and our chief, to liaise with the medical authorities and take all action to stop the disease spreading. It was an anxious period for everyone concerned. The crucial need was to locate any possible contacts and ensure vaccinations were given. The department's officers carried out their tasks with real efficiency and urgency, and our team, directing them, was enormously proud of their efforts."

He personally supervised the disinfection of the university buildings involved and the Parkers' family home, including bedding and clothing, which were buried deeply in a landfill site. He also supervised disinfection of the isolation hospital in which Janet died. Her mother contracted the disease as well, but survived; her father died of a heart attack after visiting her in hospital.

Many of his Victorian and Edwardian predecessors would have carried out similar work to calm panic, and to isolate and contain the feared disease. He concludes: "It was pleasing and gratifying to be able to report on the conclusion of the outbreak of the close and worthwhile co-operation that took place between the medical profession and local authority."

Chronology 1970s

1970

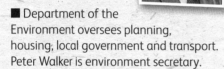

June. Edward Heath wins an election for the Conservatives.

■ Department of the Environment oversees planning, housing, local government and transport. Peter Walker is environment secretary.

■ Social Services Act, following the Seebohm Report. New social services departments. Medical officers of health to transfer from councils to the NHS.

1971

■ Power strikes and blackouts.

■ Britain signs Treaty of Accession for the European Community.

1972

■ Housing Finance Act. Help for slum clearance. Switch to home improvement from building following 1968 white paper.

■ Clay Cross councillors' rebellion.

■ Local Government Act (implemented in 1974) brings structural re-organisation. Council water responsibilities shifted to water authorities, which are privatised in the 1980s.

■ John Poulson bankruptcy. Twenty people are ultimately jailed.

1973

■ Britain joins the European Community. Oil crisis. In the Budget, £1.2bn is slashed from public spending. Power, rail and miners' strikes. Three-day week.

1974

February. Miners' strike. Hung parliament. Harold Wilson forms minority Labour government.

October. Labour wins election by three seats.

■ Flixborough chemical plant explosion kills 29.

■ Labour freezes council rents, extends security tenure and repeals much of the Housing Finance Act. Powers of Housing Corporation extended.

■ Health and Safety at Work etc Act. Control of Pollution Act. Sex Discrimination and equal pay legislation.

1975

February. Margaret Thatcher wins leadership of the Conservative party.

March. James Callaghan becomes Prime Minister. High inflation and sterling crisis. Chancellor Healy demands £1bn spending cuts. Standard Spending Assessments and the Housing Investment Programme – the first central government capital control on housing.

■ Race Relations Act.

1977

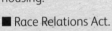

■ Fireman's strike. Lib-Lab pact keeps Labour in power.

■ Homeless Person's Act.

■ Silver Jubilee. Twenty-five year celebrations of the reign of Elizabeth II.

1978

■ 'Winter of discontent'. Plans to abolish the House of Lords removed from the Labour manifesto.

■ Last fatal case of smallpox in the world, Janet Parker, Birmingham medical photographer.

1979

March. Scotland votes for devolution, Wales no.

May. Conservatives win general election. Margaret Thatcher is the UK's first female prime minister. Michael Heseltine is environment secretary.

Don't just hope for a better life. Vote for one.

VOTE CONSERVATIVE X

Storms and markets

T he UK's political landscape changed dramatically on 4 May, 1979, when Margaret Thatcher, the country's first female Prime Minister, entered Downing Street. Not in a mood to compromise, she soon laid out the stall for her 12 years in office. The consensus, 'one nation' politics of the Wilson and Heath era were over. Following a decade of industrial unrest, she would be tougher with the trade unions. Her approach to local government would be equally radical, particularly as masterminded from 1987 by her uncompromising transport, environment and trade and industry secretary Nicholas Ridley.

For the public sector, the 1980s saw a massive withdrawal of capital funding and the tendering of local authority services, beginning with direct labour organisations, refuse collection and street cleansing. Later, came the creation of internal markets for care services and the NHS, involving what was called a 'purchaser-provider split'.

A market paradigm was also applied to housing policy. Capital, 'bricks and mortar' subsidies were withdrawn so that council house building dramatically reduced across the UK, ultimately to almost zero, while personal subsidies in the form of housing benefit increased exponentially. This approach was endorsed by the influential Duke of Edinburgh's inquiry into housing (something like the Royal Commissions of the 19th century) in the middle of the decade. Of more direct relevance to EHOs working in private housing were the removal of fair rents and security of tenure for new tenancies.

The decade was marked by a series of environmental disasters. The Chernobyl nuclear power plant explosion on 26 April, 1986 was the world's most serious nuclear accident. It led to the contamination of pastureland by radioactive isotopes across Europe, including the UK. Milk was removed from the food chain and restrictions were imposed on the movement and sale of sheep.

In response to the accident, the Local Authority Radiation and Radioactivity

Chernobyl, Ukraine – site of the world's most serious nuclear accident

Monitoring, Advice and Collation Centre was set up by the Association of District Councils, managed by the Institution of Environmental Health Officers. Working with the National Radiological Protection Board, its role was to gather data from food samples, to determine the extent of radioactive contamination and to provide baseline data on safe levels, in case there should be another nuclear accident in the crumbling energy-generating infrastructure of the Soviet Union.

The following year, the King's Cross fire in London killed 31 people and severe storms felled trees and disrupted power supplies. In 1988, headlines were dominated by the Piper Alpha oil rig explosion, which caused 165 deaths, and the bombing of a Pan Am airliner over Lockerbie – in this case, local EHOs were responsible for setting up a temporary mortuary.

In the 1980s, the UK public became particularly sensitised to food hazards. In 1984, a severe outbreak of salmonella in the Stanley Royd hospital in Wakefield, Yorkshire, caused a national outcry. Some 355 patients and 106 members of staff were affected, with 19 frail and mentally ill old people dying. EHOs had warned that the kitchens were poorly-maintained and infested with rats and an inquiry into the outbreak referred to "comments made to us that the IEHO regarded many hospital kitchens throughout the country as being unsatisfactory". The incident gave impetus to a successful IEHO campaign for the removal of crown immunity from hospitals from food safety inspection (see below). EHOs were also heavily involved in unravelling national scams to divert knacker meat into the human food chain, in Operation Meat Hook.

Several new food hazards became prominent. The public was alerted to the dangers of listeria in pâté, soft cheeses and chilled and ready-to-eat foods and even of salmonella in baby milk. In 1989, an outbreak of botulism affecting more than 30 people was linked to contaminated hazelnut yoghurt. The previous year, a junior health minister, Edwina Curry, had caused a temporary collapse of the UK egg industry by saying that "most of the egg production in this country, sadly, is now affected with salmonella". The comment cost her her job.

Propelled by 24-hour broadcast media, food scares now developed by the hour, if not the minute. Environmental health services had to be well-informed and quick on their feet. An electronic mail service, Telecom Gold, introduced in 1982, facilitated a rapid hazard notification system. It was the precursor to a secure intranet service run by the CIEH, EHCNet. The largest of the decade's food scares, the BSE crisis, began unobtrusively in November 1986 with the identification of a new animal disease by the Central Veterinary Laboratory. Dominating the final years of the decade, BSE undermined public confidence in scientific and regulatory systems and had profound political implications.

The Environmental Health Officers Association (EHOA) had ended the 1970s with important professional issues settled. General Council had decided, following extensive consultation, that the professional body should become an 'institution' and that, to underpin its professional credentials, it should apply to the Privy Council for a Royal Charter. A Royal Charter is "a deed granted only by the Crown giving special powers, rights, privileges and immunities. It is usually made to public institutions, universities and similar bodies. A charter is effectively a constitution governing an organisation's objects, activities and methods of operation."

HRH Princess Alexandra visited the new CIEH HQ, Chadwick House, in 1984

A new title, the Institution of Environmental Health Officers, came into use in 1981. It was also determined that registration as a charity would be sought. For the purposes of professional registration, two previous bodies were merged into the Environmental Health Officers Registration Board. Reflecting changing job roles, the former Commercial and Industrial Group became a 'centre'.

The IEHO also ushered in a new era in 1981 by saying goodbye to its old headquarters, Grosvenor Place. It purchased The Convent, in Rushworth Street, Southwark – a four-storey property with space for meetings and a council chamber. Thought by some to be haunted, the convent was de-consecrated and christened Chadwick House, honouring the IEHO's first president, Sir Edwin Chadwick.

A Royal Charter duly arrived in 1984. The Queen approved the recommendation of the Privy Council on 25 June and a reception was held at the Café Royal on 28 November to celebrate the event. In the same month, the IEHO was registered as a charity. From now, the IEHO would be subject to scrutiny by the Privy Council. The IEHO greeted a royal visitor that year when HRH Princess Alexandra called in to see a plaque that she had unveiled at the Centenary Congress in Brighton, the previous year. She was shown around Chadwick House by IEHO president Roy Emerson and his predecessor, Mick Archer, and their wives and introduced to the staff.

In the late 1970s, the EHOA had noticed that basic training for food handlers was woefully lacking, identifying this as a cause of a significant growth in food poisoning. Accordingly, it decided to organise courses nationally through Cleaner Food Centres, initially with St John Ambulance. The IEHO's commercial arm, in support of the growing charity, was now flourishing. By the end of the 1980s, it would be issuing more that 5,000 basic food hygiene certificates annually. Intermediate and advanced food qualifications were introduced and a basic health and safety certificate. The staff contingent was now more than 50, so that three separate offices were required to accommodate overspill.

After 23 years of service, Ken Tyler, who had followed Reg Johnson, resigned as general secretary in 1985, to be replaced the following year by Bob Tanner, who was given a new title: chief executive. The IEHO was seeking to raise its profile and appointed Bill Randall, a professional journalist, as a PR officer. Mr Randall decided to launch a new, weekly publication, paid for by recruitment advertising, to complement the monthly journal, *Environmental Health*. Thus, *Environmental Health News* came into being. Its first issue arrived, in September 1986, with a story about a famine in housing improvement grants. From the beginning, *EHN* was a popular and commercially-successful publication, which not only paid its way but contributed to the charitable income of the professional body.

There was a great deal of important professional housekeeping in the 1980s. During a congress in Scarborough, the International Federation of Environmental Health was set up in 1985 (see below). The centre and branches were reorganised, following the publication of a working party report chaired by Graham Jukes and the IEHO's technical committee was replaced by subject-specific housing, environmental protection, food and occupational health committees. A working party on environmental health education produced an important report in 1984. The report called for a 'cradle to the grave' professional education and development system, measures to help graduates from other disciplines and members of ethnic minorities enter environmental health. It emphasised the importance of the publication of research and called for a review of the qualifications of technical support staff to ensure that routes were provided that would enable them to progress and qualify as EHOs.

Many local authorities had begun to employ technical assistants – their number would grow to 1,000 over the decade. The IEHO was involved in the validation of training schemes for the technical assistants over the decade, including specialist diplomas in acoustics and health and safety. Six universities were now offering an environmental health degree, including King's College in London, producing more than 100 graduates a year. At the end of the decade, General Council determined that professional membership of the IEHO would only be by a degree or its equivalent. In a parallel development, the Privy Council approved changes to the charter and byelaws, so that applicants for corporate membership after January 1990 would have to pass the Assessment of Professional Competence (APC). It could be argued that, by these means, the professionalisation of environmental health was now complete.

Tony Lewis, CIEH head of policy and education, comments: "Some EHPs may look upon professional requirements that began then as being burdensome. But they are all necessary. Practical training logbooks, experiential learning portfolios, professional examinations, the APC and, later, Assessment of Professional Development (APD) were all designed to shift the focus towards enduring professional competence."

Mirroring the higher profile of food safety, health and safety roles for local government increased in the 1980s. The Health and Safety Commission transferred 100,000 premises to local authorities for enforcement and the important Control of Substances Hazardous to Health Regulations were introduced. The Association of District Councils established an advisory group of 22 chief EHOs, appointed on a geographical basis, under the chairmanship of Roy Emerson, IEHO president. The purpose of this group was to advise and support the development of environmental health policies within the local government political framework.

What we now call environmental politics grew in prominence over the decade and the institution played its part as an expert and advisory body. For example, the IEHO joined the European Environment Bureau and gave evidence to the Royal Commission on Environmental Pollution on the implementation of best practicable environmental options. The IEHO's radiation monitoring working party published a report on risks to health from radon and it became a fully-subscribed member of the standing conference on investigation of air pollution.

As the democratisation of the Soviet bloc countries in central and eastern Europe progressed, then under secretary Graham Jukes represented the IEHO in Frankfurt at a World Health Organisation (WHO) meeting to support environmental health development. This would lead to a full decade of engagement with WHO. Concern mounted on the possible health effects of exposure to environmental lead (leaded petrol was banned in the UK in 1998). To inform the debate, the IEHO produced guidance in 1983.

Another major issue of the 1980s was the under-regulation of the UK meat industry – in particular, poor hygiene in abattoirs and the trade in unfit or illegally-slaughtered meat. In 1982, a prosecution of meat traders was the culmination of Operation Meat Hook (see below), a joint investigation between detectives and EHOs from three counties. The IEHO set up a review group and submitted

Being indiscreet about eggs lost Edwina Currie her ministerial post in 1988

evidence to a government committee of inquiry on the meat inspection service, calling for stronger legislation. Clive Wadey, IEHO assistant secretary, also worked successfully with the European Food Law Association (the IEHO was in effect the UK section of EFLA), MEPs and the Trading Standards Institute to influence food legislation emanating from Brussels.

In 1984, following the Stanley Royd hospital salmonella outbreak, Mr Wadey was heavily involved in a campaign to remove crown immunity from food safety enforcement for hospitals. He worked with Richard Shepherd MP, who introduced a private member's bill. The NHS (Amendment) Act 1986 made NHS food preparation an area subject to the provisions of food legislation. Mr Shepherd thanked the IEHO and Mr Wadey in the House of Commons.

Two years later, EHOs would be inundated with inquiries from the press and the public worried about contracting Salmonella enteridis after Edwina Curry's rash pronouncement on eggs.

Nationally, the IEHO benefitted in the 1980s from a chief medical officer who valued the role of EHOs. An appointment going back to the 1850s, the CMO is the government's most senior health official, advising the Privy Council. The annual report, in 1988, of CMO Sir Donald Acheson acknowledged the contribution of EHOs to health in the community and called for the creation of directors of public health in every health authority. Sir Kenneth Calman, his successor in the post from 1991 to 1998, was also to be supportive of the profession. It was Sir Kenneth who instigated a multi-disciplinary approach to public health and gave impetus to measures allowing non-medically qualified professionals to become directors of public health.

The avoidable health damage caused by tobacco was increasingly coming onto the radar as a policy issue. At the IEHO's annual general meeting in 1985, a motion was approved calling on the Institute to join the professional medical associations and lobby the government to ban all tobacco advertising. Other motions advocated an end to the discharging of plutonium into the Irish Sea and a reduction in SO_2 levels by 30 per cent by 1993.

High in the CMO's in-tray from the mid-1980s were two issues that partially served to define the decade. The initials BSE, standing for bovine spongiform encephalopathy, first appeared in the UK press in 1986. With each year, its dreadful implications became more apparent, both for the national cattle herd and for people, in the form of a degenerative and untreatable human brain condition: new variant Creutzfeldt-Jakob disease (nvCJD). Tough and decisive policies on the feeding of cattle and the handling of potentially infected meat were called for – invariably, they were introduced late, due to political reticence and the foot-dragging of MAFF.

It was not until 1989, when hundreds of tonnes of contaminated meat had entered the food chain, that MAFF and the DoH recommended the compulsory removal and staining of infected material from carcasses in abattoirs. BSE was a public health issue spanning two decades. In the 1990s, the future CIEH chief executive Graham Jukes was to submit evidence to the Phillips inquiry into BSE.

The ominous initials AIDS and HIV also entered the national consciousness. It was in 1986 that the government launched a national campaign warning the public not to 'die of ignorance'. The IEHO regarded the issue as being of great concern to its members. Against some opposition, it ran seminars on the threat and, in 1987, published guidance notes for EHOs, authored by Ian Gray, who would later become a CIEH principal policy officer.

Food safety

Ned Kingcott, chief EHO at the DHSS from 1981, was an influential figure in this period, bridging the worlds of enforcement and policy making. His role was to run the DHSS's food hygiene and microbiological safety group, which he describes as "an interesting but rather quiet backwater of a large government department". He notes: "Apart from occasional food hazard incidents, we rarely saw ministers or the chief medical officer… yet within a few years, food safety would become a major political issue." The reasons? Concerns over campylobacter and listeriosis and the emergence of *E. coli 0157* as a major threat.

Mr Kingcott recalls an incident in 1985 that put national surveillance and control systems to the test and demonstrated how sensitised the public now was to food safety. Some cases of salmonella were linked to Farley's baby milk – microorganisms could now be rapidly typed and incident and outbreak data quickly interpreted, so that outbreaks could be identified from a relatively few cases of illness. The baby milk was immediately recalled but the bad publicity put Farley out of business.

In the 1980s, EHO still had duties in connection with abattoirs, which required practical training. Joanna Tawel recalls: "In the late 1980s, I was a student EHO at Colchester BC and spent most of my time in the local slaughterhouses. I think I must have done in excess of 800 hours there over the three-year diploma. There were some interesting occurrences, like the time four slaughtermen chased a pig around the clean area of a slaughterhouse after it had escaped from the dirty part.

"As a young person on my own concentrating on inspecting viscera, or plucks (while awaiting the duty EHO's appearance), this was quite scary, not least because of the extra noise of the men shouting and the pig squealing like a banshee above the noisy slaughtering process and Radio 1 at full blast. Of course there were the usual student tales of little green men in the cupboards, insects in the carpet turning out to be fluff and illegal cesspool outflows."

On the ground, EHOs were doing the dogged work that they had always done to weed out corner cutters and wrongdoers at the dodgy end of the meat trade. David England remembers a cause celebre of the 1980s, Operation Meat Hook. He notes: "In early 1980, EHOs at South Bedfordshire District Council became seriously concerned about the sources of meat supplied by a butcher in Houghton Regis. Astute detective work by myself and chief EHO, Terry Oliver, established that some of the supplies were coming from a knackers yard in Wigston, Leicestershire, more than 60 miles away."

A local EHO and his wife, posing as a courting couple in a lane next to the yard, witnessed suspicious unloadings from an unmarked Transit van. Further surveillance found that diseased and injured animals were being brought there and put into the food chain.

Mr England continues: "The police were contacted and arrangements were made to tail the van. One night in May 1980, the EHO, who was also

Food technology became more sophisticated and food safety a major political issue

called England, and his wife followed the van from Wigston to Houghton Regis where it was parked overnight under police observation."

Events quickly unravelled. An illegal national supply chain involving the addition of fake hygiene stamps to unfit meat was uncovered. The perpetrators were arrested and one jailed. There was a national furore. A well-known company that had used the dubious meat in its beefburgers and sausages had to destroy tons of stock. Mr England concludes: "Since 1980, there have been several similar incidents. However, given the lucrative rewards of meat crime, EHOs will continue to deal with it until the problem is finally and permanently solved."

Don Oliver, a Suffolk EHO, investigated a similar knacker-meat scam in the East of England – it was a common and lucrative crime until the staining regulations came into effect. Mr Oliver writes: "The first line of enquiry was to the butcher who had the county council contract to supply meat to schools and residential homes. We then traced a paper trail via meat brokers to the premises where the problem arose."

He explains: "Knacker meat destined for dog food was bought at 10p per pound, mixed at a ratio of three-to-one with fit meat, wrapped in polythene and deep frozen. It was sold on, with each broker adding to the price, until it was eventually sold by butchers at £1.50 per pound. The unthawed meat was prepared and delivered to schools."

Mr Oliver recalls that tact and secrecy were required when uncovering the trade. He had to be sure that no-one involved would be tipped off and there was a real danger of physical violence at the hands of the perpetrators. Premises were always inspected with the police and information exchanged on a 'need-to-know' basis.

Legislation introduced in 1969 had only required the sterilisation of knacker meat before sale. But this requirement had been unevenly observed. In the wake of the Meat Hook cases, the IEHO set up a meat legislation review group and held meetings with MAFF and the Department of Health. It worked with Norman Atkinson MP, who introduced a private member's bill and lobbied parliament during its committee stage. Supported by all parties, Mr Atkinson's Food and Drugs (Amendment) Act strengthened the Food and Drugs Act of 1955. It increased penalties significantly for food crime, making it possible for cases to be heard in crown courts and tightened controls on the disposal of unfit meat.

The power of the media

Another practitioner who entered the profession in the 1980s and went on to achieve prominence is Lisa Ackerley. A chartered EHP and PhD, Ms Ackerley became acknowledged as one the of the UK's leading food safety experts, through her role as a consultant, expert witness and media commentator – she was probably the first 'TV EHP' and the first to gain a Wikipedia entry. Dr Ackerley graduated with a first class BSc (Hons) in environmental health from the University of the West of England in 1984 and then worked as an EHO for Cherwell DC in north Oxfordshire for a modern-thinking chief EHO, who was keen to encourage her to progress her career.

In the 1980s, female practitioners still encountered some ingrained prejudices against women in a profession that was dominated by men. She comments: "One memory that sticks in my head is being asked by a chief EHO at an

Lisa Ackerley – TV expert and the first
EHP to have an entry in Wikipedia

interview for a trainee EHO in 1982: 'What would happen if you got pregnant?' To which I answered 'I guess I would have a baby'. I didn't get the job. It went to a male candidate."

She left the local authority world to become an academic. Initially senior lecturer in food law and practice at the University of Greenwich, she was subsequently appointed as the first visiting professor in environmental health at the University of Salford and completed her PhD at the University of Birmingham on food hygiene. Later, Dr Ackerley taught on the MSc environmental health course at King's College, University of London. Whilst at the University of Greenwich, she became a Winston Churchill Fellow, and was awarded a travelling bursary to visit the US and Canada to research the implementation of food hygiene systems based on hazard analysis critical control points (Haccp).

In 1988, she set up a successful food and health and safety consultancy, Hygiene Audit Systems, and from the 1990s she began to do expert witness work, for example as a crown expert at the fatal inquiry in the 1996 *E. coli* outbreak in Lanarkshire. Throughout her career, Dr Ackerley has passed on her experiences to her peers through presentations at CIEH events and she has travelled as far as the US and South Africa in order to present papers.

She started to make regular media appearances in the 1990s and appeared on programmes as diverse as BBC Radio 2's Chris Evans show, talking about dishcloths, and on investigative BBC TV shows such as *Watchdog*, *Rogue Traders* and *Rogue Restaurants*, *Save our Holiday*, *Secret Tourist* and *Holiday Hit Squad*. In *Rogue Restaurants*, she was filmed in a van commenting, in layperson's terms but from a professional perspective, on unhygienic practices captured by live secret cameras in restaurant kitchens.

These consumer protection shows were extremely popular. It's not surprising. The camera loves food, it loves yucky things and it loves jeopardy and resolution – the narrative of a problem successfully resolved, thanks to an outside intervention. The BBC's *A Life of Grime*, which began in 1998 and was specifically devoted to EHOs (although based on an elastic definition of their work), became one of television's most popular 'reality shows'. One character from the show, Edmund Trebus, a Polish former prisoner-of-war who filled his house with rubbish, became a national figure. EHOs were shown dealing with the eccentric and frail old man patiently and tactfully, although he accused them of being Nazis.

Some practitioners fear that appearance of environmental health on prime-time television risks misrepresenting or 'dumbing down' the profession. Dr Ackerley disagrees. She comments: "TV and radio shows are a great way of promoting public health messages and raising awareness of our profession. I never know what to expect when appearing on a programme. I may be asked to comment on swimming pools, drinking water, playgrounds, fire safety, buffets, pests, or cleanliness and housekeeping. It's the wide remit of the environmental health degree that makes this possible and, following on from the consumer shows, I'm now often asked to comment on news programmes. I'm passionate about representing the profession in this way."

Pigeons, radon and wheelie bins

Julia Atkins recalls: "I was working at Enfield Council in 1980s when we had a complaint regarding a 'pigeon lady'. Apparently the lady had been taking in pigeons and people had also seen rats in the vicinity. It was causing a nuisance to neighbours. I went along and knocked on the door. An elderly lady answered in dirty, old clothes. As she spoke to me, she itched and scratched. I saw that she had large boils all over her face. She also seemed to have difficulty breathing. (I thought the itching, boils and possibly some of the breathing problems could be because of bird mites, if the allegations were true).

"She reminded me of how someone may have looked with the plague! I explained that we had received complaints about rats and accumulations. I was concerned about her welfare and I explained that I would need to go into her house to either dismiss the allegations, or to provide her with help if required.

"I went back the next day and entered the house. Rather than taking in a few pigeons and keeping them in a coup, the 'pigeon lady' had lots of pigeons that were free flying around the whole of her house. She had given them names. There must have been approximately 60 and some were getting in through the roof. I walked on the carpet and it crunched.

"I also couldn't see the colour of the carpet. It was covered with pigeon droppings which must have been about an inch thick. The furniture was the same, grey with excrement. It was unbelievable that she had been living and sleeping in there, probably for many years. I explained that it was hazardous to her health and the accumulations would need to be cleared. There was also evidence of rats and a rodent treatment needed to be carried out.

"We served notice. The house and garden were treated for rats. The accumulations were cleared, a hole was repaired in the roof and the pigeons were taken away. We tried to get some help for the lady from social services in order that it didn't happen again, tried to obtain for her some medical help and to educate her not to take in more pigeons."

Diana Adamson, a female EHO who qualified in 1982, trained and worked with Wakefield MDC which includes Castleford. She recalls: "As a young female in the mainly male-dominated office (apart from Janet Russell who quickly moved to Kirklees) the men may have taken pity on me. I covered a reasonable area of Castleford and a pit village.

"After about 12 months, we had a shake-up of office areas and I took over the Knottingley area from Keith Gibson (recently retired from Leeds). It included the then infamous Warwick Estate. Festooned with piles of rubbish and surrounded by open fields, the estate was occupied by many single parent families. Day and night, packs of dogs roamed loose. It was a smoke control area but nearly every house emitted smoke.

"From my photographs, it is evident that the residents thought nothing of dumping refuse and abandoning cars in their own backyard. Inspection chamber covers would regularly go missing which would inevitably lead to blocked drains – luckily though Wakefield WDC offered a free drain-clearing service in those days! Although I had been at Wakefield five years by this time, the Warwick Estate was a shock and a battle to improve!"

Former Northamptonshire EHO Maurice Jones was a technical specialist in an age in which environmental health was increasingly requiring scientific disciplines. He recalls: "The radioactive natural gas, radon, was known to be a problem in Devon and Cornwall. In 1987, the IEHO set up a working party, under the chairmanship of Dr Martin Courtis, who had represented the IEHO on the National Radiological Protection Board. EHOs across the country were asked to survey for radon by placing monitors in domestic premises … Money was tight but Kettering and the neighbouring borough of Wellingborough agreed to take part." The results were worrying – in Wellingborough, three out of six test results were above the action level. "This was a shock," he recalls. "Would it blight investment in the borough? How would the residents react?"

Grants were available from the NRPB for monitors. The approach taken was to be as open and transparent as possible, using the local media to provide information and advice. A radon-

Ron Charnick, health director at Wealden DC, was the man who brought the wheelie bin to Britain

affected area was declared and a radon working party set up for authorities around Northamptonshire – subsequently, radon, sourced to ironstone deposits, was found in Kettering and most other parts of the county. Mr Jones's open approach was exemplary – don't hide the science, use the media rather than being led by it, be open about risk-evaluation and keep people up to date. MAFF could have learned a lot from him in dealing with the BSE crisis.

Much of the work of EHOs is not glamorous but has enormous implications for health and quality of life. As director of health and housing at Wealden District Council, Ron Charnick took on a highly-stretched refuse service with limited resources, working across a large area. Looking abroad, he came up with a solution that was new to the UK – the use of kerbside plastic dustbins on wheels that could be lifted hydraulically into refuse vehicles. Mr Charnwick had to source the bins, run trials, consult with members and unions and talk to the treasurer's department about the legal implication. It was a long, arduous process but, at length, Wealden was the first council to introduce what would become known as wheelie bins.

The assistant secretaries

Stephen Battersby – joined the EHOA when it had cramped offices over a bank

Stephen Battersby, past president of the CIEH, writes: "When I went to work for the Environmental Health Officers Association in 1980, the process of acquiring Chadwick House in Rushworth Street SE1 had just started. The offices were still above a bank at 19 Grosvenor Place. My office overlooked the Queen's back garden. The offices were cramped, although there were only about a dozen full-time staff. My colleague, Clive Wadey, had successfully pushed for our job title to be changed from technical officer to assistant secretary – a designation that matched Civil Service grades.

"The move to the former convent, Chadwick House, was completed in early summer 1981, but the contractors were still on-site and the basement refurbishment (which would include the library, post and printing room) was still to be completed. Until completion of the work, it was used as a store for equipment, as well as files and archives. That time also coincided with a summer cloudburst and flooding. I recall wading up to my knees to rescue association documents, including ledgers that were 100 years old.

"The work of the assistant secretaries – Clive and myself – was under the aegis of the technical committees of the General Council. General Council in those days, which had more than 50 members, was much involved with the work and management of the organisation, including overseeing the annual conference. Yet, at the same time, the assistant secretaries were given considerable freedom. I dealt with housing and pollution issues, and Clive with food, occupational and general health issues. Ken Tyler, as general secretary, was heavily involved in the educational aspects of the association and liaising with the Privy Council, so that the organisation would become the Institution of Environmental Health Officers and, soon afterwards, obtain its Royal Charter.

"One of the first major projects I was involved with was as secretary of the area improvement working party, which had been established to report on the contribution of environmental health to urban renewal, building on the Housing Act 1974. A report containing proposals for a new 'fitness standard' was published with a fanfare at the annual congress in 1982. It was the glossiest publication that the organisation had published.

"Annual congress, held alternately in the North and on the south coast, was the grand event of the year. The four-day event had a packed programme and was attended by up to 1,000 delegates, and almost always included at least one government minister as keynote speaker. The event was run with military precision – a General Council briefing on the Sunday included a full schedule of who would meet and look after every speaker. During the 1980s, we also instigated one-day seminars on topical issues and then we made use of the council chamber (a former chapel) as a cheap venue to run low-cost members' workshops.

"A lot of housing policy work revolved around houses in multiple occupation (HMOs). There were private members' bills (for example from MPs Joe Dean and Jim Marshall) to improve HMO legislation. We worked closely with other housing organisations such as Shelter and CHAR – as a result of the housing work, I got to know Bill Randall who had started *Inside Housing* at the Institute of Housing. It was during one of our chats that the idea of a new publication, *Environmental Health News*, was hatched (see below).

"An increasing need for information for members and policy papers was identified, leading to a series of professional practice notes – for example, on different kinds of HMOs. With the help of colleagues involved in legal casework, such as David Ormandy, a housing law newsletter was started. This was in addition to the annual environmental health report, based on returns from almost all local authorities.

"There was a lot of work with the parliamentary vice presidents, such as Chris Smith (now Lord Smith), Peter Archer QC and Simon Hughes. One politician with whom I worked closely was the redoubtable Baroness Joan Vickers. It was she who, after a fatal HMO fire in Kilburn, succeeded in amending legislation to place the first duty on local authorities to deal with larger HMOs.

"Much time was also spent trying to improve pollution control legislation. It was fortuitous that Mick Archer as president was also a member of the Royal Commission on Environmental Pollution. In addition to the perennial issue of noise and providing information to the DoE there was considerable liaison with the Alkali Inspectorate, which then became HM Inspectorate of Pollution and moved from the Health and Safety Executive to the DoE. This work revolved around determining how local authorities could be given more effective powers to prevent air pollution. One eventual outcome of this work was to be Part 1 of the Environmental Protection Act 1990.

"The organisation was increasing its influence and activities. By the end of the 1980s, despite the former loggia in the garden being converted into office space, the search had begun to find new, larger premises. The number of EHOs working in business and commerce was growing steadily, mostly in the area of food safety. Clive worked closely with the Commercial and Industrial Group to dispel the widely held notion that its members were EHOs who had gone over to the 'dark side'."

The 'yellow pages'

I n 1985, the Institution employed Bill Randall, a freelance journalist, to provide press and publicity expertise. Mr Randall had been editor of *Inside Housing*, a magazine published by the Institute of Housing. Within a year, he had persuaded the IEHO to launch a weekly publication entitled *Environmental Health News*. It succeeded a monthly newssheet published in the journal, affectionately known as the 'pink pages', which was produced by John Tiffney.

The new publication was printed on yellow paper and became known, inevitably, as the 'yellow pages'. It contained several pages of news and crucially, several pages of job advertisements. Thanks to the topical news it carried, the national media was also interested and its stories often appeared on TV and in the national press, resulting in greater public awareness of the profession.

In 1986, production methods were primitive. Copy was typed, before being faxed or couriered by motorbike to a typesetters to be made into galleys, which were cut and pasted into position, to be made into film, for printing. The galleys were sent

The profession's weekly magazine carried job ads

to the printers each Wednesday evening. Computer technology and the internet subsequently took over.

Mr Randall was joined from the outset for one day a week by Deirdre Mason, another well-known journalist, and subsequently by his daughter Sophie. Other key players were Marlene Davies and Claire Brown, both of whom played a vital part in *EHN* becoming a desktop publishing venture, freelance writer Peter Mason (no relation to Deirdre) and Paul Prior, who sold advertising. An important function of *EHN* was to carry job opportunities in both the public and private sectors, and the income generated made a substantial contribution to the professional body's revenue streams.

The CIEH bought out Mr Randall's share in 1995. Sophie Randall became editor, eventually handing over to William Hatchett in 1998, by which time she and Claire Brown were joint managers of the publishing department. In 2000, the yellow paper was discontinued in favour of white. A daily edition of *EHN* was published, for the first time, for delegates at the annual conference of 2001. There were now CIEH and *EHN* websites.

In 2009, a searchable jobs website was added. The following year, it was decided to merge the weekly and monthly publication, then called *Environmental Health Practitioner*, into a single title. Retaining the name *EHN*, the new magazine was initially bi-weekly and then monthly. It was supplemented by a weekly e-mail newsletter, *EHN Extra*, produced by digital editor Tom Wall, who exploited the new possibilities provided by social media. The magazine's art editor was Jon Heal. Advertising manager Paul Prior's career went right back to the beginnings of *EHN*: he had worked with Bill Randall.

The global dimension

Designed to spread the aims and expertise of the environmental health profession across national boundaries, the International Federation of Environmental Health came into being in 1985. It began when Eric Foskett persuaded IEHO president Roy Emerson to hold a meeting in his hotel room during the annual conference in Brighton. The date was 24 September. Attending the meeting from the IEHO (representing England, Wales and Northern Ireland) were John Tiffney, Roy Emerson, Eric Foskett and Clarence Phenix; from the Royal Environmental Health Institute of Scotland were Dr TS Wilson and Bernard Forteath; from EHOA (representing the Republic of Ireland) were Fred O'Brien and Jerry Heraghty; from Malaysia came HJ Sulaiman and from Sweden, Barbara Blomberg.

Mr Foskett's enthusiasm was infectious, although the hurdles of lack of money and great distances were formidable. With the support of Mike Halls of REHIS, he worked tirelessly to get the project off the ground. The federation formally began on 29 August, 1986 in London, when the first council meeting was held. Australia's professional body, Environmental Health Australia, joined the IEHO, REHIS and EHOA as the fourth founding member. The First World Congress was held in Sydney, Australia in 1988. Mr Emerson was invested as the first president in the presence of the Governor General of Australia and representatives of 17 different countries. Further congresses took place in Brighton in 1991, Kuala Lumpur in 1994, Aberdeen in 1996, Stockholm in 1998, Oslo in 2000, San Diego in 2002, Durban in 2004, Dublin in 2006, Brisbane in 2008, Vancouver in 2010 and Vilnius in 2012. The 2014 congress was scheduled to be held in Las Vegas.

The IFEH's 39 members are not individuals but organisations in countries where administrative, legal and environmental health services are similar to those in the UK. Members can be part of regional groups serving Africa, the Americas, Europe, Asia and Pacific, and the Middle East. Each member appoints representatives to a governing body, the Federal Council. The IFEH also has associate and academic associate members.

In addition to its founding IFEH membership, the CIEH has been extremely active in promoting twinning arrangements between its regions and other environmental health bodies around the world. The first twinning arrangements were made between the CIEH Northern Ireland region and Tanzania, where a degree course was established in Dar Es Salaam University and a library named after a popular EHO, Clarence Phenix. A trustee and past CIEH chairman, John McCandless, was heavily involved in fund-raising and in getting the arrangements in Tanzania off the ground.

Further twinnings followed – the East Midland region with Uganda, CIEH Wales with Rwanda, London region with Jamaica, the North-West region with Zambia and the North-East region with Kenya. The CIEH also set up an International Special Interest Group, a body encouraging CIEH members to get together to promote and discuss international topics.

A charity that aims to improve water supplies and sanitation in the developing world, Water for Kids, was begun by EHOs Stewart Petrie, David Clapham and Natasha Franklin following a visit to Peru in 1995 on an EU-funded programme to combat cholera. Water for Kids continues to go from strength to strength and has a strong participation from the environmental health community.

International champion

Eric Foskett OBE, who died in 2001, is much missed both in the UK and around the world. Mr Foskett qualified as a sanitary inspector in 1940 and served in the Royal Army Medical Corps (RAMC) from 1940 to 1946. In 1961, he was appointed deputy chief public health inspector in Stoke-on-Trent and then moved to Manchester, where he became director in 1974, remaining until his retirement in 1985.

Mr Foskett was elected vice chairman of the
Midland Centre in 1967. From 1968, he joined
the North-Western Centre council, serving as
chairman and president and was also chairman
of the Greater Manchester branch. He was
an adviser to the Association of Metropolitan
Authorities, a member of the health and safety
advisory body, Hela, and helped to set up
the senior officers' management course at the
University of Birmingham.

For the IFEH, he served as honorary
secretary, honorary vice president, honorary
co-ordination officer and president. He
was the IFEH delegate on the CIEH visit
to Russia in 1992. An Eric Foskett Award
is now presented at each IFEH world congress. It goes to an individual or an
organisation having made a notable contribution to the federation.

Eric Foskett – man with a vision for
international environmental health

Chronology 1980s

1980

■ Unemployment passes two million. Direct labour organisations brought under tighter control. Extension of the right-to-buy for council tenants.

■ Black Report links ill health and poverty.

1981

■ Environmental Health Officers Association becomes the Institution of Environmental Health Officers. It is granted a Royal Charter in 1984.

■ Riots in Brixton, followed by Southall, Toxteth, Moss Side and parts of the West Midlands.

■ Royal Wedding of Charles and Diana.

■ Social Democratic Party (SDP) begun by the 'gang of four'. Development Corporations begin in Merseyside and London.

■ AIDS first recognised by US Centers for Disease Control.

1982

■ Falklands War.

■ Women's peace camp begins at RAF Greenham Common, where cruise missiles are to be located.

■ Big Conservative losses in local elections. Labour takes Greater London Council.

1983

June. Conservatives win by a 144-seat majority. Social Democratic Party polls only half a million votes fewer than Labour.

■ Griffiths' report into the NHS recommends an 'internal market'.

1984

■ Year-long miners' strike follows threatened pit closures. More than half of Britain's mineworkers stop work.

■ IRA bomb blows up the Grand Hotel in Brighton during the Conservative party conference in October.

■ Privatisation of British Telecom.

■ Stanley Royd hospital food poisoning outbreak kills 19 people. Public Health (Control of Diseases) Act tightens the law.

1985

- Broadwater Farm estate riot.
- Duke of Edinburgh's inquiry into British housing.

1986

- Abolition of metropolitan counties and the Greater London Council.
- Chernobyl nuclear power station explosion.
- BSE identified as a cattle disease.
- EHO seminars highlight challenge to health from AIDS.

- CIEH publishes a weekly magazine. *Environmental Health News.*

1987

June. Conservatives win election by 100 seats.

October. 'Black Monday' economic collapse.

- Fire spreads through King's Cross station in London, causing 30 deaths.

- Storms kill 17 people.
- Health Education Authority begins.
- Crown immunity for food prosecution lifted from hospitals.

1988

- Piper Alpha oil rig explosion. BSE crisis intensifies. DHSS splits.
- Housing Act. Fair rents abolished for new tenancies. Rent subsidies reduced. Housing Action Trusts can take over council estates.
- Access to private finance for housing associations. Accelerated transfer of council stock.
- Sir Donald Acheson chief medical officer's report, *Public Health in England*.

1989

- NHS review proposes GP fund holders and self-governing hospitals. Compulsory competitive tendering for council services. Food safety white paper.
- Local Government and Housing Act. Housing renewal areas. Mandatory renovation grants for owner occupiers and landlords.

The 1990s

A shrinking
world

J ohn Major, an unassuming former Lambeth councillor, became leader of the Conservative party and Prime Minister in November 1990, with a mandate to heal the UK's wounds. Memories of the May poll tax riots were still fresh. One of Mr Major's first acts was to appoint Michael Heseltine as his environment secretary, with the task of replacing the poll tax with a structure for local government finance for England, Scotland and Wales that would enjoy general acceptance. The result, the council tax, introduced in 1993, was based on a banding system relating the tax paid to property value. This move sealed the Prime Minister's popularity. In April 1992, he captured an election from the Labour party, led by Neil Kinnock, with a small majority.

The Institution of Environmental Health Officers (IEHO) began the decade in a buoyant mood. New legislation would have important implications for EHOs. The Environmental Protection Act of 1990, combined with The Control of Pollution Act, would underpin their environmental protection work and establish a new regime for pollution control, through permitted processes. Five years later, HM Inspectorate of Pollution, the National Rivers Authority and 83 waste regulation authorities would be amalgamated into the Environment Agency, a national regulatory body tasked with ensuring safe drinking water and a clean environment. Also in 1990, a Food Safety Act consolidated and replaced most previous food safety legislation. And in 1993, the so-called 'six pack' of health and safety regulations transposed European directives into detailed UK law.

The IEHO's commercial operations, particularly the delivery of certificated training in food hygiene, were now flourishing. It would be inconceivable now for a professional body to operate without computers. The IEHO was no exception, using its growing income to upgrade its IT capacity. In due course, e-mail largely replaced the letter. Typewriters disappeared. Soon, everyone had a computer on their desk – instant communication spanning vast distances was possible.

In 1991, a new chief executive, Terry Brunt, took over from Bob Tanner.
The policy and resources committee approved a new vision statement. It was for
the IEHO "to continually improve the safety and health of the public through
a membership known to be competent for the task and with a professional
organisation respected in the community and able to serve its members from a
sound resource base".

That year, two years after the collapse of the Berlin Wall, a delegation including
the new president, John Tiffney, had visited Russia to explore opportunities for
establishing environmental health contacts. Widening the profession's sphere of
influence would be a theme of the decade, especially following the establishment of
the IEHO as a collaborating centre with the World Health Organisation (WHO)
in 1993, under the leadership of Graham Jukes. Collaborating centre status was
to be renewed five years later in . The following year, the CIEH was asked to
contribute to the organisation of the WHO's Third Ministerial Conference on
Environment and Health in London. The CIEH hosted a meeting of all WHO
collaborating centre directors and ran a
parallel NGO conference on the theme
of water.

Assistant secretary Ian MacArthur (see
below) was tasked with two important
missions in the post-Cold War world.
He first travelled throughout the WHO's
European region, including eastern Europe,
to produce an overview of environmental
health practice and a series of policy guides.
Next, seconded to the WHO to fulfil a
two-year contract with the Department for
International Development, he prepared
environmental health action plans for six
countries in central and eastern Europe and
Asia, including former Soviet republics.

The CIEH moved to Chadwick
Court in Southwark in 1993

In 1992, General Council agreed to cease
to offer a diploma in environmental health. This
completed the move to the provision of an all-
graduate profession. Continuing professional
development was now to become compulsory for all corporate members, requiring
documented evidence of at least 20 hours of study each year. Assignments were
set each month in *Environmental Health Journal*. Practical training logbooks were
introduced for all students.

The IEHO, which had been working from three sites, in Rushworth
Street, Great Guildford Street and Borough Mews, had outgrown its office
accommodation. In 1993, it moved into a new headquarters Chadwick Court, in

Hatfields, Southwark, on a 20-year mortgage. Now, all employees including those employed by *Environmental Health News*, formerly based at Black Prince Road, were situated under one roof. As well as office accommodation, the new HQ provided for a council chamber, seminar facilities, committee rooms and a library. There were several advantages to the Waterloo area – in particular, the proposed London Underground Jubilee Line extension and the construction of the new Eurostar Terminal at Waterloo, as well as proposals for the renovation of the South Bank area of London.

This was the year of another important event. In July 1993, Her Majesty the Queen granted the organisation a new title, the Chartered Institute of Environmental Health (CIEH). The new president, Andrew Banfield, was able to break the news at the annual congress in September (see below). From now on, corporate members were able to use the designatory letters MCIEH and Fellows FCIEH.

The country was in recession – 16 September, 1992 had seen the national catastrophe of 'Black Wednesday'. Following the excitement of the achievement of a new title and the purchase of its new building, the CIEH now had to face up to some major financial problems. They arose from a projected income shortfall at the end of 1993. Reluctantly, the decision was made to reduce budgets and staffing in 1994. The financial position had stabilised by 1995, helped by the appointment of new resources director, Gary Ince.

General Council determined to focus on the 'core business' of providing services to members pertaining to professional, technical and educational issues, and to reduce involvement in peripheral activities. The CIEH and its commercial arm, Chadwick House Group Ltd, were restructured and new financial regulations and standing orders were agreed. There was a focus on ensuring stability in income generation and controlling expenditure. A new chief executive, Michael Cooke, was appointed, replacing Linda Allen, who had effectively filled the role of acting chief executive.

The 1990s will be remembered as a green decade, with the terms climate change and sustainability becoming current. The CIEH was increasingly working in the international arena, with organisations such as the WHO and the European Commission. It opened an office in Brussels in 1990.

Nick Wilson was the IEHO's assistant secretary for pollution and housing from 1992 to 1995, working with Ian MacArthur, Cathy McKenzie and Howard Price under the direction of Graham Jukes. Nick represented the CIEH in Brussels. He also, like Ian MacArthur, carried out country reviews for WHO. He recalls: "It was a glamorous life for a humble assistant secretary and in hindsight, I was lucky to be given such opportunities."

The massive United Nations Earth Summit held in Rio in June 1992 was one of the key events of the decade. It was attended by 255 governments and thousands of representatives of non-governmental organisations. A precursor to the Kyoto

The United Nations Earth Summit, held in Rio, put environmental politics onto the world stage

summit five years later, Rio produced a climate change convention and Agenda 21: a detailed set of goals for the next century.

Local authorities and groups of activists set up local Agenda 21 groups to create blueprints for how their areas could become more sustainable. Many EHOs were involved.

Nick comments: "My work was framed in part by the 1992 Rio declaration. Its first principle proclaimed: 'Human beings are at the centre of concerns for sustainable development. They are entitled to a healthy and productive life in harmony with nature.' This statement chimed well with the IEHO's motto 'friend of the human race' – a high bar of aspiration."

He argues that, after Rio, the CIEH became a significant player in thought leadership, helping to embed the principles of sustainable development into national and local government policy, for example by encouraging the creation of local Agenda 21 groups.

Nick recalls: "Life at Chadwick House (later Chadwick Court) was never dull. Visits from fellow EHOs, think tanks and ministers kept us busy. During this period, under Graham's leadership, the policy team built up strong working relationships with central and local government, enabling us to put an EHO with the relevant experience in front of senior civil servants to make our case to change or introduce new legislation. This blend of diplomacy and 'real world experience' changed the course of many parliamentary bills."

The Rio Earth Summit in 1992 led to the creation of the United Nations' Habitat II programme, designed to promote healthier and more sustainable settlements worldwide, and this, in turn, led to a series of daughter conferences, at which the CIEH was able to exert an influence. Assistant secretary Howard Price attended 'prepcons' for Habitat II in Kenya in 1995 and New York a year later, this time accompanied by fellow assistant secretary Ian MacArthur.

Howard recalls: "In studying the negotiating text for New York, Ian and I realised that the draft Habitat II Agenda that was being drawn up did not adequately acknowledge linkages between the environment and health. Consequently, we drafted some amendments, including a 'principle' on health. One sunny morning, we were sitting in the cafe of the UN building. At the next table were some US delegates and we gave them what we had written. As a result, our text was included in the Agenda. Although it was subsequently amended, some of our words were adopted at the final Habitat II conference held in Istanbul later that year."

In 1993, the Maastricht Treaty, signed the year before, came into effect. Perhaps the most significant milestone of John Major's premiership, it brought the European Union into being and, to the horror of Eurosceptics, led to the creation of a single EU currency, the Euro. By the middle of the decade, Major's government was faltering, riven by disputes over the UK's role in the EU and allegations of 'sleaze'. But this period saw important legislation. For example, the Meat Hygiene Service was set up to run meat inspection services in the UK, taking over from local authorities.

The crisis caused by BSE was reaching its peak. At the beginning of the decade, the chief medical officer, Sir Donald Acheson, had boldly declared that 'beef is safe' but, as the 1990s progressed, bringing poor policy-making and inept crisis management from MAFF and the DoH, this reassurance came to ring hollow.

In 1995, a link between BSE and nvCJD, a degenerative human neurological disorder, was established and two million cattle over 30 months old were slaughtered to remove them from the food chain. Ultimately, the crisis led to the deaths of at least 29 people from nvCJD and the slaughter of 4.4 million cattle.

The loss to the UK economy was estimated at £3.7bn. MAFF came out of the crisis and the foot and mouth epidemic of 2001 badly. It ceased to exist in 2002.

The dying days of the Major administration brought, in 1996, a Noise Act, which defined excessive noise levels for enforcement purposes and clarified night-time seizure powers and a Housing Act abolishing mandatory renovation grants. That December there was a food safety scandal, echoing the Stanley Royd case of 1984. Nineteen people died as a result of eating meat products contaminated with *E. coli 0157* bought from a butcher's shop in Lanarkshire. The shop's manager and staff had been ignorant of protecting cooked food products from cross-contamination, in this case from a deadly bacterium.

Tessa Jowell was the UK's first minister for publich health

It was one of the UK's worst outbreaks of food-borne illness. An inquiry, conducted by Professor Hugh Pennington, identified cross-contamination of raw meat and cooked meat products as being the cause of the infection. The inquiry recommended the licensing of butchers' shops, with a requirement for training in hazard analysis and critical control points (Haccp). Weaknesses identified by the inquiry in food safety would strongly influence the James Report, which recommended the setting up of a new non-ministerial department, the Food Standards Agency.

Nothing could save John Major from a decisive defeat in 1997. A refashioned Labour party – it had been re-branded 'New Labour' – swept to victory by a landslide, 179-seat majority. In the hot seat was a young, personable Prime Minister with a constant smile: former barrister Tony Blair. This was to be another mould-breaking, radical administration, favouring market economics but with a softer, more conciliatory tone than Thatcherism.

Critics from the right said that New Labour favoured a 'nanny state'. Smoking, excessive drinking, an unhealthy diet and sedentary lifestyles were now the biggest threats to the UK's health and New Labour initially seemed more willing than previous governments to promote 'lifestyle politics'. Mr Blair's 1997 cabinet contained the UK's first minister for public health, Tessa Jowell MP (in 1999 the post was downgraded to junior minister status).

Acknowledging the huge costs to health and the economy of tobacco, the government produced a *Smoking Kills* white paper in . The introduction of a total ban on smoking in public places was now a major policy objective for the CIEH. It was also pressing the government for the mandatory licensing of houses in multiple occupation. In 1999, a health white paper, *Saving Lives*, was published, alongside a reducing inequalities action report.

The documents represented a break from the past. The white paper focused on cancer, coronary heart disease and stroke, accidents and mental health. It referred to local authorities as partners in health policy and to reducing 'upstream' cause of ill-health as well as treatment. Just how unequal in economic and health terms the UK had become was underlined in the Acheson Report, authored by the former CMO in 1999, and by the Marmot Report a decade later.

The last year of the decade also brought the Water Industry Act which fulfilled a long-running CIEH campaign by banning the disconnection of domestic water supplies for debt.

Another theme of the Blair administrations was constitutional reform. Following referenda, elected national legislatures were established in Wales, Scotland and Northern Ireland. In Scotland and Wales, but not England, a unitary map of local government was imposed. English local authorities were required to adopt an executive mayor or cabinet by the Local Government Act 2000. This was the final death knell of the environmental health committee, although services could benefit from a 'portfolio holder' at least partially representing their interests. Also in 2000, following a referendum, an elected executive mayor heading an assembly took over the strategic running of London. The first mayor was Ken Livingstone, who stood as an independent. Mr Livingstone spoke at the 2001 CIEH annual conference.

New Labour scrapped the compulsory competitive tendering of council services but brought in something rather similar – best value. Like the Thatcherite Conservatives, it favoured the 'marketisation' of public sector services, allowing them to opt out of traditional democratic structures, for example as foundation hospitals or city academies. New Labour's motto, in the early days, was 'what matters is what works'. There was lots of measurement in all areas of social policy through 'performance indicators' and there were many exhortations to 'join up' services. Poverty and deprivation were euphemistically termed 'social exclusion', a problem which was given its own unit. Although Mr Blair had criticised them in opposition in the 1990s, under his government, quasi-autonomous non-governmental organisations or 'quangos' proliferated.

The CIEH was pleased that the new government included a public health minister. Before the general election, it had promoted an 'empty beds' campaign to stress the role played by environmental health in reducing sickness and its subsequent cost to the NHS. The CIEH now published *Agendas For Change* (see below), a detailed manifesto that had been in preparation since 1996. The work had been undertaken by a highly-respected group of experts, including chief executive of Belfast City Council Brian Hanna, a former EHO and future CIEH president. It was designed to make recommendations on the future of environmental health.

Interestingly, many of the report's recommendations would be fulfilled more than a decade later, not framed by sustainability but by the public health reforms introduced by the Health and Social Care Act of 2012 (see next chapter). This piece of legislation, in the spirit of *Agendas For Change*, would return public health powers formerly vested in the NHS to local government and task councils with producing strategic 'health and wellbeing strategies'.

In , recalling its 19th-century roots, the CIEH commemorated the 150th anniversary of the passing of the 1848 Public Health Act – the legislation conceived by Sir Edwin Chadwick that had brought the inspector of nuisance and medical officer of health to local government. It published an illustrated booklet, *150 Years of Public Health*. The publication was complemented by a paper presented at the annual conference in Harrogate by Mike Eastwood of Liverpool University. In the same year, an annual Reginald Johnson Memorial Lecture was launched to honour the memory of Reg Johnson, who died in 1997 and had been the longest serving general secretary (1950-1977).

The decade ended symmetrically with a new mission statement: "To maintain, enhance and promote improvements in public and environmental health." The Privy Council approved a number of amendments to the charter and by-laws, one of them introducing a new term, environmental health practitioner (EHP), for those who were professionally registered.

The change of name acknowledged the fact that CIEH members no longer worked exclusively in the public sector. There was a significant membership in the private sector and in government agencies, and a growing membership drawn from other disciplines. The opportunity to apply for chartered EHP status also came into effect in 1999. By 2009, there would be 2,000 chartered EHPs. The CIEH was looking forward to the next decade – task groups recommended widening CIEH membership beyond EHPs, a review of centres and branches, and the creation of a research fund.

Lights, music… action

Andrew Banfield presided over a new era and a change of name

A ndrew Banfield OBE, was a student public health inspector at the Royal Borough of Kensington in the 1960s. He became chairman of General Council in 1989. In 1993, he was elected president of the IEHO for a three-year term. It would be during his presidency that the Institution would adopt its new name, the CIEH.

He recalls: "One of the duties of the president was to make the presidential address, a keynote speech, at the annual environmental health congress. Congress was the most important annual event for the profession and attracted delegates from all over the UK and abroad.

"It lasted for a week and consisted of a number of professional and social events. It was a chance to meet old and new colleagues, to learn of the latest professional trends and for the government to make 'an announcement'. Usually, a minister would have made the trip with a civil servant.

"Before the 1993 congress, quietly behind the scenes, the IEHO had been working on an amendment to its Royal Charter to change the name of the professional body. The new name was to reflect the changing role and indeed wider horizons for environmental health and the profession. It was to be announced by me before making my address. On the opening day of congress, the main hall in the Bournemouth International Centre was full. At the appropriate moment, I rose and addressed the audience as follows: 'Welcome everybody to the last congress of the Institution of Environmental Health Officers (dramatic pause) and to the first Congress of the… Chartered Institute of Environmental Health.'

"Lights and music accompanied this announcement. It was all rather theatrical but it went down particularly well and for me, personally, was the high spot of my long association with the CIEH. The name change was a demonstration of the way forward and gave me great joy. We had gone from strength to strength as a professional body since 1883, I reflected, as the sound of applause filled the venue. Who knows what the future may hold?"

Town and county

Julie Monk, head of environmental services for Eden District Council, began her varied professional career at the beginning of the decade. She writes: "Like many, I stumbled into environmental health, not really understanding what I was letting myself in for. In 1989, I went for a job as a trainee trading standards officer at Westminster City Council but was offered a post as an environmental health technical assistant. My interests were in food safety and consumer protection, having a B.Tech in food technology and a degree in consumer science.

Julie Monk moved from crowded Westminster to the rural idyll of Cumbria

"That was no preparation for my new role in the commercial team and my new district in central London which covered Soho and Covent Garden. Thankfully, I had a really good manager, Peter Kemp, and a good team who not only showed me the ropes but also helped me navigate the one million tourists that descend on the area every day – a daunting sight when you have been brought up in Cumbria!

"On my first day, I was introduced to the office computer and a huge pile of yellow forms, each containing details of service requests, inspections and revisits. Being happy to carry bags, take notes and take photographs, I got to follow EHOs into some of the best restaurants, hotels and clubs in the world. I also saw inside the Houses of Parliament, which we were allowed to inspect.

"Giant cockroaches, rats and dead bodies were not uncommon sights in a typical working week (although not in the Houses of Parliament). Take-aways and restaurant chains were a growing phenomenon, along with Filofaxes and pagers. Legionnaire's disease had a high profile and we spent many hours on the roofs of office blocks and hotels, peering into swimming pool-sized cooling towers – thankfully, the view compensated for the vertigo.

"Westminster had not supported a student placement for many years, but the chief EHO had made a case for two students, one full-time student and a part-time position for me. I enrolled at King's College, London, at the campus in Kensington, and was one of the first part-time students there on a relatively new course. I attended university for one or two days per week for three years.

"Another part-time student from a London borough and I were at an advantage. Having been there, seen it and done it, we could relate our practical experience to the theoretical lectures. Looking back, it seems a better route than full-time education, as I was able to hit the ground running at the end of the course. A big difference between environmental health qualifications then and now is the absence now of slaughterhouse training. It seemed to go on forever. I spent some time in a Cumbrian knackers' yard, the images of which are still etched in my mind.

"As part of my student training, I went back to my home town of Penrith in Cumbria for two weeks of rural work experience with Eden District Council. The contrast could not be more pronounced – from a packed, sweaty Tube on a daily basis to a trip out over the Pennines with the pest control officer. As we pulled up outside the Orton Chocolate factory in the Eden Valley, I thought: 'This is the life for me'.

"I graduated in 1994 and continued to work in Westminster's commercial team. But shortly after, I was asked to move into the pollution team, mainly focusing on air quality. The issue of PM_{10} pollution was hitting the headlines and, keen to lead the way, the council invested in a PM_{10} monitor. We took the packaging off and gathered round it in awe. This led me back to King's College, where I worked with a couple of research students measuring filters and interpreting results.

"I now saw in the back of the 'yellow pages' an advert for a job vacancy in Eden District Council's pollution team. I couldn't let that opportunity pass and was pleased to start there in early 1997. Cumbria has an excellent branch of the CIEH, which I became involved with as a student training co-ordinator and then as chair. Eden has supported a student post every year. They are always great assets for the department, and I have continued to be a student mentor and mark experiential learning portfolios.

"My career at Eden moved through pollution to food and health and safety to housing. For the past three years, I have been the head of environmental services. As one of my first tasks, I created a part-time technical officer/student post, which was offered to promising and enthusiastic admin officers. I currently spend one day per week for the District Council Network, in a national role, on housing policy and advice.

"I am really proud to be part of the profession. I am a chartered member and constantly learning. The task is enormous – the focus of government moves at such a rapid pace and we have some interesting times ahead, but I am lucky to have a fantastic team and to live in such a beautiful place."

The plotlands

It would be a mistake to think that all poor housing conditions had been dealt with by the 1990s. Many EHOs will recall, in this era, entering property that was 'filthy and verminous', in the jargon of their job, perhaps because it had been occupied for decades by the same person, who was now frail and elderly. Joanna Tawell was a principal EHO in Rochford DC's residential team. She describes the area as a "rural backwater, close to Southend". In this environment, she encountered kitchens which still had 'coppers' and Belfast sinks, outside WCs and, in one case, gas lighting.

There were also overflowing cesspits and neglected caravan sites, where carbon monoxide poisoning, which can be fatal, was an ever-present danger. Her south Essex district, fringing the Thames, contained once-squatted communities known as 'plotlands', the residents of which lived in improvised

Improvised houising in the 'plotlands' of Essex kept EHO Joanna Tawell busy

shacks made from timber, asbestos cement and corrugated iron.

She writes: "I recall a number of serious filthy and verminous premises that required warrants to enter and where we carried out works in default on a regular basis. One, in particular, was in a block of flats and required this form of action four times a year for three years. We just could not get one lady to understand the issues at all – the smell of her flat was atrocious because she didn't let her cats out and never cleaned up after them. How she didn't burn the flat down I'll never know. There was always a huge pile of part-smoked cigarettes and ash in the living room.

"There was also a client we nicknamed 'the letter writer' because of the letters in green ink on his walls. Latterly, he became known as the 'Neutradol man' because of his attempts to cover up the smell and flies in his kitchen. Most of the filthy and verminous cases had mental health social workers. Sometimes, we were able to resolve the issues before legalities got in the way but often the problem was the client not taking their medication and lack of social services resources to chase up the case properly – a very sad scenario."

She adds: "Other memorable cases included another lady in the sticks whose husband had died and she was so bereft that she didn't do anything about the maintenance of her bungalow until the settee fell through the wooden lounge floor. When I inspected the property it had no inside WC, no hot water, a badly-leaking roof and dangerous electrics. It would have required almost total rebuild - only the timber structure was sound. In the end, the plot was sold and a new bungalow built on it. This was one of several interesting cases where the preferred option came out as demolition and rebuilding. There were (and still are) a number of asbestos shacks in the district – 60 to 80-year-old properties on old plotland sites."

Port health

The vital environmental health specialism that deals with helping to make sure that imported food is safe and preventing infectious diseases from coming into the county began in the 19th century when port sanitary authorities were established, under the wing of local government. The following century brought air travel – port health authorities could either be docks or airports, offering new, often challenging, work settings.

Jon Averns, later port health and public protection director for the City of London Corporation trained as an EHO back in the 1970s at South East London Technical College. He had his first brush with port health (which tends to resemble the uniformed services in its traditions and work practices) when his class visited London's Royal Docks: "We were greeted by Lieutenant-Commander Alan Game who immediately reprimanded me for wearing training shoes."

He began work in the riverside borough of Greenwich in the 1980s, as a district EHO. Work practices in those days would not have been hugely different from the Victorian era. The docks were in sharp decline but a technological revolution was coming in – containerisation. Jon specialised in food safety, working at the Victoria Deep Water terminal, a small container facility on the Greenwich Peninsular.

He recalls: "In those days, there was no such thing as a dedicated inspection facility or sampling plans for high-risk products. We would simply go out onto the container park with a couple of stevedores, open the container doors and take whatever samples were required."

By the 1990s, he was a port health inspector with the London Port Health Authority, based at Sheerness. He remembers: "The Olau Line ferry service from Vlissingen carried a variety of foods including Danish bacon, Dutch eggs and oysters, Polish sausages, top quality calves' livers and lots of frozen apple strudel

"In the main part of the docks, fruit was the speciality with produce from Chile, New Zealand, South Africa and Israel. Salmonella in imported eggs was an issue, there were problems with pesticides in fruit, and cargoes contaminated by hydraulic fluid and oil, but we had a varied and healthy diet!"

The next decade would bring even more dramatic changes to the profession. In 1993, the European single market began and border controls were relaxed. Jon was now working at the Thamesport and Tilbury container ports. The safety of products of animal origin was of particular concern.

He writes: "We now had to comply with strict European legislation, and were audited by the Food and Veterinary office (FVO). I have seen grown men quaking in their boots as the formidable female German auditor from the FVO scrutinised every last piece of paperwork."

In , he became port health director for London. This year was the centenary of the Association of Port Health Authorities. He recalls a celebration hosted by the City of London Corporation on a luxury Thames cruiser. He says: "I had been reassured by the caterers that they would give the delegates an experience never to forget. They were right; half way through the main course many people started to realise that their chicken breasts were raw inside and as we drew up to the quay our port health launch appeared alongside and white-coated port health officers boarded the vessel to commence an investigation into the incident.

"I sweated for the next two or three days, but fortunately my fears proved unfounded. I was later in the invidious position of having to act as both enforcement officer and client of the caterers – I settled for a hefty discount."

The 2002 foot and mouth disease outbreak led to the Food Standards Agency demanding a step change in the way in which imported food controls were delivered. Since half of the UK's food was imported, there was plenty of work to do and The Association of Port Health Authorities was an influential organisation. Jon travelled to the US to advise the American peanut industry in Georgia and to Thailand to explain the intricacies of European food law to its exporters.

He remembers gruelling but pleasurable CIEH Port Health Centre study tours of the era, such as, early morning visits to the fish and meat markets of Manchester, organised by chief port health officer, Bill Besford-Foster, followed by visits to food factories, government departments and ports.

"The hospitality of the tours was always top class. I shall never forget a visit to the Ambassador's house in Dublin, and the trip around the Guinness Brewery followed by copious quantities of the black stuff.

He adds: "Inevitably, port health has evolved. We now see more sophisticated adulteration of foods from industrial dyes to melamine in milk powder, as well as a range of veterinary residues in products of animal origin. Proposed changes to European food and feed legislation will be challenging, and in London we look forward to the opening of the London Gateway container port, which will become the biggest port in the UK."

Our man in Kazakhstan

In the 1990s, it was the important job of Ian MacArthur, CIEH assistant secretary, to make the world of environmental health smaller, forging links with the EU in Brussels and pursuing the goals of the profession in Central and Eastern Europe.

He writes: "I joined the IEHO from Edinburgh City Council as the assistant secretary for health and safety in November 1991 when Vic Reeves and the Wonderstuff's song, *Dizzy*, was at the top of the charts. The song had resonance for me. The day I first walked in to the creeky old former convent that stood as the Chadwick House HQ on Rushworth Street, the institution's first fax machine was being installed. It was, in many ways, a sign of the times and of things to come, as over the following 10 years the world became more connected and faster paced.

"My initial brief was to follow the whirlwind that was Linda Allen. Linda was a feisty, but ever-so-clever Glaswegian who managed the food and health and safety portfolios in her under secretary role. For me, this meant interpreting, influencing and developing guidance for the six-pack of European health and safety directives

Sofia in Bulgaria early 1990s – destination of assistant secretary Ian MacArthur

that were part of the completion of the single market in 1992. This called for lots of contorted meetings and hours writing up minutes and policy responses in longhand for subsequent typing. Occasionally, it meant trips to Brussels and Strasbourg, where our retained European lawyer, Amanda Cleary, would glide us effortlessly through the corridors of power.

"Those trips over the channel were combined with absorbing Graham Jukes' enthusiasm and ambitions for the IEHO to engage with the WHO to address public health issues on an international scale. In late 1992, when Graham offered me the opportunity to be seconded to the WHO's European Office in Copenhagen, I jumped at the chance. The shape of Europe had changed suddenly. Following the fall of the Berlin Wall in 1989, the state-controlled behemoth that was the USSR had fractured in 1991 and with their new-found freedoms the former Warsaw Pact countries were turning their gaze towards the west.

"The institution's vision was simple – work with the WHO to support the countries of Central and Eastern Europe on environmental health reforms. We would then have new partners and allies in an eventually expanded European Union. I arrived in Copenhagen in March 1993 to work with the passionate, awkward, but truly inspirational Xavier Bonnefoy, WHO regional director for Europe. Xavier was a former French sanitary inspector who had a vast knowledge and experience of international working, coupled with a style that had been forged in the 1968 Paris student revolts. My task was to establish a project that would develop guidance for the reform of environmental health services across Europe.

"Said quickly, it sounded OK. Think about it longer and it was head spinning! I did have some wonderfully supportive colleagues. Graham Jukes had been in the vanguard of this work and had already undertaken a review of Poland. But in truth and with hindsight, the scale of the challenge and the speed of change meant that the work had to adapt and develop almost on a daily basis.

"My first trip to Eastern Europe was a 14-day mission to Bulgaria. The capital, Sofia, suffers from decades of grey Stalinist architecture and a seemingly constant smoggy inversion created by the surrounding mountains. Despite the early seeds of economic and democratic reforms, many aspects of life had yet to accept and adapt to reformed thinking. On my first wander through the city, I could still see evidence of burnt and disused buildings marked during the 1989 Ecoglasnost protests and perhaps most strikingly, neon signs for Benetton and Johnny Walker casting shadows on the queues for bread at the general store.

"Such contrasts could be found throughout the post-communist states at this time. On a further visit to Sofia, I recall crossing the city by car on a particularly drab and dismal day, when out of the corner of my eye I caught a flash of silky red cloth and blonde hair – not something you'd normally see on Sofia's streets. On closer viewing it turned out to be a team of 'Marlborough girls' giving away cigarettes on the street. The free market had arrived in frontier land.

"I also recall a particular journey from Kosice to Bratislava in Slovakia, when we passed a Roma gypsy encampment. It was a cold, blue-sky day and boys were playing football on the outskirts of the shanty camp, as smoke rose from the tin and wooden shacks. On closer inspection, I saw the footballers were playing barefoot and yet as we got nearer to the encampment itself there were satellite dishes on the shacks. Again, the markets had moved faster than organised society could react. I spent the rest of that journey contemplating how images of consumer-led western lifestyles would be transmitted to the gypsy camp, and on how a thirst to acquire contact and knowledge from a wider world had taken precedence over basic clothing needs. It gave a real perspective to the small difference we were trying to make.

"Professionally, working with colleagues in Eastern Europe was both delightful and frustrating in equal measure. Whilst always welcoming and anxious to demonstrate their knowledge and professionalism, their openness to change was limited. I recall a particular conversation with a director of a local sanitary station telling me that whilst he understood everything I said, I should say it to someone who was under 30, as it was only they that may have the ability to change.

"During my first year at the WHO, I managed a team of experts from across Europe to visit and review the environmental health services in 27 countries, from France to Uzbekistan. The following year I spent taking their core material and converting it into an overview of European environmental health practice and, more interestingly, a set of policy guidelines for the reform and development of the services across Europe. This process exposed me to international negotiations, ministerial conferences, lobbying and seemingly endless late night re-drafts of text.

"By the end of 1994, the drafts had been accepted and published as WHO guidance and a range of successor projects had been set up to continue the programme. I found myself back in London, but now in Chadwick Court and working for the renamed CIEH.

"After three months or so of picking up various policy threads and routine duties (including most memorably giving a manual handling presentation to hardware retailers in Torbay), Graham and I put a paper to a General Council meeting in Leicester Town Hall, proposing that the CIEH should establish an independent commission to review the whole subject of environmental health and make recommendations on the profession's future direction.

"By 1995, John Major's Conservative Government was tired and local government had been squeezed by numerous reforms until it lacked any spark or innovation. To me, there was a danger of the profession being moulded by other people's

Dr Barbara McGibbon chaired the *Agendas for Change* commission

agendas. The proposed commission would help to make sense of what may lie ahead. To have credibility, it would need to be independent, therefore the CIEH would not necessarily like what it recommended.

"Not surprisingly, there was some opposition to the concept, but within six months, approval and funding had been secured and, in March 1996, the first meeting of the commission was held at Chadwick Court. Thirteen commissioners had been chosen for their individual knowledge and expertise and for their potential to become advocates for the profession. Looking at the list now, it reads like an environmental and public health *Who's Who*. Together with Graham Jukes, I acted as the commission secretariat. The commission's chair, Dr Barbara McGibbon, was a focused and unflappable leader.

"Just as essential to the success of the commission was the recruitment of David Nicholson-Lord to be its ghost writer. David, a former environment correspondent for the *Independent on Sunday*, made readable, engaging prose out of seemingly disjointed meetings in which debates and nuances could be discussed for hours. As the process developed over 18 months or so, it appeared that the group had collectively struck on something important – it was a rediscovery of the need to address the integration of environment and health under local democratic leadership. This was the single most important recommendation of the final report, *Agendas for Change*.

"I recall clearly the final drafting meeting held in Chadwick Court on the morning that the three major political parties were to publish their manifestos for the 1997 election. After the meeting, I returned to my desk to look through the manifestos. While I do not recall the promises made by the Conservatives or Liberal Democrats, the Labour document was littered with echoes of the report. It was clear that somewhere behind the scenes some cross-fertilisation had been going on between the commission and the policy team of the soon-to-be-elected New Labour government.

"*Agendas for Change* was published in July 1997. It was warmly welcomed by the government and, for a short period, provided a strong platform for the environmental health profession to realign its direction, rediscovering its connections, in particular to public health agendas. I spent the next 12 months taking the *Agendas for Change* message to conferences at home and abroad and to centre and branch meetings up and down the country.

"I completed the 1990s with more international work. The WHO had secured DFID funding from the UK government and wanted the CIEH, with its newly-established WHO collaborating centre status, to manage a two-year programme on local environmental health planning. This programme took me even deeper into Eastern Europe and Central Asia, working with local municipalities in Latvia, Bulgaria, Slovakia and Kyrgyzstan, as well as the other Central Asian states (Kazakhstan, Uzbekistan and Turkmenistan).

"Once again, this was head-spinning work that revealed immense cultural and social challenges, and at times, highlighted the most basic of environmental health needs and inequalities. I recall during one trip to Ashgabat in Turkmenistan that my local interpreter quietly complained over a long dinner that they had no water at home and that it was switched off regularly during the summer months, yet in the splendid centre of the city, fountains gushed with literally millions of litres of water.

"Whilst the local authorities that we worked with developed useful plans and some innovative funding mechanisms, in many respects, the sweeping market reforms moved at a different level. I left with the greatest concern for Eastern Europe's housing stock. The economic liberalisation and the repatriation of property from the state to the individual that followed the collapse of the Iron Curtain combined to compound the problems created by poor construction standards.

"Even today, there is little money, either private or public, for investment in the housing sector. Little or no preventative maintenance is carried out and repairs are done only on an emergency basis. Given that some 170 million people across Eastern Europe live in decaying, system-built flats, the scale of the problem is immense and the social and health pressures across the region will only increase over time.

"My years working for the CIEH in these challenging and ambitious projects were amongst the best and most informative of my working life. The fabulous colleagues I met and friends I made at home and abroad have given me a rich and diverse network that I know that I can always rely on."

Agendas for change

The report was published in 1997 and its recommendations were accepted by CIEH: "To provide a starting point for a wide ranging debate within the profession and beyond, leading to substantial reform and long-term improvements to environmental health." Two main themes emerged – inequality and sustainability. The commission concluded that unless urgent attention was paid to reducing the disparities in wealth between social classes, its vision would not materialise. Its vision also depended on the environment and health becoming integral components of sustainable development policies and on individuals accepting the need to modify their lifestyles.

The commission expressed the view that the best organisational model for the delivery of environmental health would be community-based. It should be flexible, inclusive, task-orientated and trained to think laterally as well as technically.

Recommendations

1 The UK Government should introduce legislation to give local authorities a new duty to prepare strategies for the sustainable development of their areas.

2 Local authorities should be required to secure the maximum involvement of local communities in preparing their strategies.

3 The location of public health, medicine and health promotion should be moved from the NHS to local government.

4 Local authorities should take over the task of producing the annual public report on the health of the local population.

5 Local authorities should, in collaboration with other bodies, develop techniques for integrated environmental health impact assessments.

6 Local authorities should initiate audits of the needs of local communities.

7 The development and implementation of sustainable development strategies should be a central policy of every LA.

8 Local authorities should be given a new general power to implement their sustainable development strategies.

9 Government departments should review all environmental health functions to consider how they could be modernised.

10 Local authorities should consider how existing plans can contribute to the sustainable development strategy.

11 All statutory plans should take account of the sustainable development strategy.

12 All interested parties should review the training and professional requirements that the new approach will require.

13 The CIEH should play a lead role in the review of training.

14 The national curriculum should include an awareness of health and sustainable development and promote active citizenship.

15 The government regions should prepare regional sustainable development strategies.

16 The key government departments should establish a joint unit to co-ordinate an integrated approach to policy on environment, health and sustainable development.

17 The new unit should establish a coherent national research programme for environmental health and sustainable development issues.

18 Target-setting should be based on locally-negotiated priorities and resources.

19 The UK government should encourage the integration of environment and health strategies at European level.

20 The UK government should launch an international initiative to integrate the United Nations Economic Commission for Europe and WHO strategies on environment and health.

21 The UK government should actively support the UNECE convention on public participation in environmental decision-making.

Chronology 1990s

1990

- Poll tax riots. Margaret Thatcher resigns. John Major becomes Prime Minister. Environment white paper.

- Donald Acheson, chief medical officer, says 'beef is safe' despite BSE crisis.

- Environmental Protection Act. Food Safety Act. NHS and Community Care Act.

1991

- City Challenge. Successful bids include Hulme and the West End of Newcastle.

- *Health of the Nation* white paper.

- Kenneth Calman follows Donald Acheson as CMO.

1992

April. John Major wins general election.

- 'Black Wednesday'. Run on the pound.

- Health and safety 'six pack'.

- Hove bedsit fire kills five people.

- World environmental summit in Rio.

1993

- Murder of Stephen Lawrence in south London.

- IEHO becomes collaborating centre for WHO's European region.

- Four deaths in Lyme Bay kayak tragedy.

1994

- Criminal Justice and Public Order Act.

- Single Regeneration Budget.

- Scarborough HMO fire.

- IEHO becomes the Chartered Institute of Environmental Health (CIEH).

1995

- Meat Hygiene Service begins.

- First case of nvCJD diagnosed in human being.

- Food Safety (General Food Hygiene) regulations.

1996

April. Unitary authorities in Scotland and Wales.

■ Housing Act. End of mandatory renovation grants.

■ Noise Act.

■ Lanarkshire *E. coli* outbreak kills 21 people.

■ Link between BSE and nvCJD announced. Two million cattle slaughtered.

■ Environment Agency begins. Covering England and Wales with responsibility for rivers, pollution and waste.

■ Dolly the sheep. First mammalian clone.

■ Death of Princess Diana.

1997

May. Labour victory with a 179-seat majority.

■ Tessa Jowell is UK's first public health minister.

■ James Report into the Lanarkshire *E. coli* outbreak. Leads to creation of independent Food Standards Agency.

■ Local Government Association forms from former local authority associations.

■ 'Yes' vote in referenda on Scottish and Welsh devolution

1998

■ Social Exclusion Unit report.

■ Acheson report highlights health inequalities.

■ *Smoking Kills* white paper.

■ National minimum wage legislation.

■ Liam Donaldson becomes CMO, following Kenneth Calman.

■ CIEH publishes manifesto, *Agendas for Change*.

1999

■ New deal for communities. Regional Development Agencies. Publication of Urban Taskforce report.

■ Launch of the Euro. The UK has an opt-out.

■ First elections of Scottish Parliament and Welsh Assembly.

■ Act to set up new London Assembly and elected mayor following referendum.

After 2000

The return of
public health

F or most people in the UK, the celebrations marking the new millennium were a bit of a let down. Fireworks fizzled, it was a grey, drizzly night, no more exciting than any other New Year's Eve. At least the 'Millennium Bug', a story conjured up by the world's media to evoke a computer-driven disaster, did not materialise. As the new decade began, disappointed newspapers concocted a global apocalypse caused by genetically modified foods.

For the environmental health profession, the Food Standards Agency was an important innovation. Partly set up in response to the BSE crisis and to the Lanarkshire *E. coli* outbreak, the agency would co-ordinate and audit the food safety services run by local authorities and offer advice to the public and to ministers on food issues and health. The new body would be independent and transparent, holding its board meetings in public. Unlike invisible Whitehall departments, it would be branded by an attractive logo and have a user-friendly website.

Its first chief executive was a civil service mandarin, Geoffrey Podger, who went on in 2002 to head the European Food Safety Authority and later the UK's Health and Safety Executive (see below). The FSA's chair was a well-respected scientist, Professor John Krebs. A former chair of the CIEH's food committee, David Statham, was appointed director of enforcement, ensuring a link between the important new agency and the environmental health profession.

A scare caused by dioxins entering the food chain in Belgium in 1999 had involved a rapid cross-border response and product withdrawal across the EU. In food safety and standards and environmental protection, UK and EU policies and practices were now inextricably linked. There were certain exceptions: for example, the UK did not share Europe's use of the veterinary officer in food safety enforcement, except in slaughterhouses.

In November 2000 came the finale of the BSE crisis, with the publication of the

16-volume Phillips report. The report had taken three years to produce, at a cost of £26m. The BSE saga had dominated the world's news in the late-1980s. It began inauspiciously, when an unusual degenerative brain disease was reported from a UK dairy animal in 1987. BSE was identified by hurriedly conducted cutting-edge science as a type of transmissible spongiform encephalopathy caused by an infective agent called a prion that is not killed by heat. The incubation period is up to eight years.

BSE in cattle, it transpired, may have been caused by feeding the animals meat and bone-meal from contaminated sheep. The first slaughterhouse controls were introduced in 1989. The following year, John Major's environment secretary John Gummer was involved in a much-criticised publicity photograph, designed to reassure the public and to bolster British farming interests. Father and child were shown eating beef burgers. By then, we were soon to learn, BSE had already crossed the species barrier to humans through people consuming infected beef.

The BSE crisis led to four million cattle being slaughtered and a cost to the economy of billions

The statistics associated with the outbreak are shocking – four million cattle slaughtered, a cost of billions to the UK economy and 166 human lives lost from a connected human illness, nvCJD. The Phillips inquiry strongly criticised MAFF for its failure to react to the event in a timely or transparent way throughout the crisis – almost half a million infected cattle had entered the food chain before controls on high-risk offal were introduced.

The CIEH had offered its full co-operation to the inquiry. Graham Jukes and Nicholas Hibbert, ex-chair of the CIEH's meat legislation review group, gave evidence. They pointed out that regulations on removing high-risk material had lacked guidance and that the government message at the time that eating beef was 'safe' had undermined official controls.

An editorial published in *EHN* on 3 November, 2000 commented: "One of the main lessons to be learned from the Phillips report is the importance of good regulation. It is now clear that the BSE crisis gave rise to a series of poorly thought-out and inadequate measures, and that the people enforcing regulations were not consulted and were given little guidance. It is not surprising that they failed... In a rational world, advice to government would be based on the best information and science, untainted by political or economic considerations;

government departments would talk to each other and consult with key players before issuing practical, proportionate and enforceable solutions; and concerns about regulations would be listened to and acted upon. The public would never be blandly assured that a product was safe to avoid damaging an economic interest group."

The implications of the crisis were profound. It had a major influence on European food policy and reduced the public's confidence, perhaps irrevocably, in the integrity of politicians and scientists. The public scares that blew up over dioxins and genetically modified food in 1999 were certainly intensified by the BSE episode. The public was more aware of food dangers than ever.

At the turn of the millennium, the CIEH's trading activities were profitable. Revenues from Chadwick House Group Ltd, its trading arm, increased to £7.5m, generating a surplus of £1.8m. The CIEH now provided 25 vocational training courses in 63 countries. Michael Cooke was followed as chief executive in 2000 by Graham Jukes, initially as an interim successor.

In 2001, Brian Hanna succeeded David Purchon as president. Mr Hanna chaired an important commission, which reported in 2004, on the future of the profession. Devolved UK legislatures were on the way. The CIEH set up offices in Northern Ireland and Wales, run by directors Gary McFarlane and Julie Barratt. They soon made a significant impact, forging partnerships with key players and ensuring that the CIEH was viewed as an important player in public and environmental health.

Concerns about low student numbers at the beginning of the decade led to a campaign to attract more entrants to the profession. At the annual conference in Bournemouth in 2001, which attracted more than 1,000 delegates, the first ever parallel new professionals' conference was held.

Brian Hanna, CIEH president, chaired a commission on the profession's future

It was repeated the following year at Harrogate. A new publication, *Journal of Environmental Health Research,* was launched and *EHN* showed off its new website. But the Bournemouth conference was shocked by an appalling event – live news was relayed to delegates, including US visitors, of the 9/11 terrorist attack on the twin towers of the World Trade Center in New York.

Severe flooding had affected England and Wales from the autumn of 2000 and lasted well into the following year. The 'freak' weather – the most rainfall ever recorded – was attributed by environmentalists to climate change. As well as the planes flying into the towers, another disturbing visual image would come to represent 2001 – burning carcasses. An outbreak of foot and mouth disease that swept across England from February was far more severe than that of 1967. It delayed the general election, which was won by New Labour in June. The crisis was to cost the UK economy an estimated £8bn.

The disease had first been identified in February at a pig abattoir in Essex and took until September to bring under control, with the help of the army. More than 10 million cattle, sheep and pigs were slaughtered. The television news each night showed scenes of horror – mounds of carcasses being burnt in pyres and pushed by bulldozers into huge burial pits. Some communities in the North-East and North-West were badly affected by smoke and odour nuisance and there were fears about the contamination of water supplies.

Large areas of the countryside were quarantined and cordoned off. If proof was required of the need for an environmental health profession, 2001 – with its floods, leaching burial pits and black smoke billowing from funeral pyres – provided it abundantly. Later in the decade, in 2007, a smaller foot and mouth episode in Surrey was caused by the escape of the virus from two nearby veterinary laboratories – EHOs and trading standards officers were heavily involved in the handling and containment of the outbreak.

The Phillips report published in 2000 had blamed MAFF for its poor handling of BSE. A repeat performance over foot and mouth was the last straw. MAFF was abolished in June 2001, its functions absorbed by a new Department for Environment, Food and Rural Affairs, led by Margaret Beckett. To the surprise of many, Ms Beckett's environmental responsibilities did not include local government, housing and planning, which, since 1970, had been the mainstay of the environment portfolio. These were transferred to a new Department for Transport, Local Government and the Regions.

Preventing meat crime is a recurring theme for EHOs (health marks can be faked or misappropriated and weak links found in complex food chains involving abattoirs, food plants and brokers). In the early 2000s, it cropped up again. Recalling Operation Meat Hook in the 1980s, officers in Rotherham and Amber Valley uncovered large-scale food frauds (see below). In both cases, the local authorities attracted positive headlines in the national press and secured prison sentences for the perpetrators.

In 2003, local government received new powers through the transfer of liquor licensing responsibilities from magistrates. There was also good news for port health officers. Following their lobbying, the Food Hygiene (Ships and Aircraft) Order made food hygiene regulations applicable on ships and aircraft. In 2003, the government set up a new body to co-ordinate contingency planning for disasters and communicable disease control: the Health Protection Agency. Communicable disease was increasingly international. It was the HPA which made the UK's plans – effectively, as it turned out – for the SARS virus in its first year and a feared flu pandemic in 2008. Fears of pandemics were much in the news. A keynote speaker at the CIEH's Best of the Best conference in Nottingham in 2008 was Lindsey Davies, national director of pandemic influenza preparedness for the DoH.

Under New Labour, health was receiving historically high levels of funding and there was a policy focus, initially, on public health. Derek Wanless, a former senior banking executive, was asked by chancellor Gordon Brown in 2001 to review NHS spending on acute health services and to find ways of reducing it. A second Wanless Report, in 2003, called for investment to reduce health inequalities and to extend preventive services to the most disadvantaged, in order to save money later on treatment.

The CIEH had submitted evidence to 'Wanless two', arguing that environmental health should be at the heart of a new public health agenda because of its primary role in ensuring decent housing, clean air, nutritious and safe food and a safe working environment. With the Health Development Agency, which had been set up in 2000 to gather evidence for public health intervention, it produced a vision statement, *Environmental Health 2012*, setting a framework for widening the role of the profession. It also made a detailed submission to the 2004 public health white paper, *Choosing Health*.

The CIEH was growing in influence, locally and nationally. For example, in 2004, chief executive Graham Jukes was appointed to the government's Sustainable Development Task Force, a body at the heart of national policy making. However, as New Labour progressed through its second term and into its third, some of its promises were to be unfulfilled. In 2005, large cuts were to be made to the NHS budget. The number of primary care trusts was slashed by half, jeopardising public health policy many feared, and the HDA, which had promised so much, was abolished.

Student numbers picked up as the decade progressed, with new BSc and MSc courses accredited. The education and professional standards team produced a new core curriculum to broaden the focus of environmental health education. It allowed students to undertake work-based training outside local authorities. For new students, an experiential learning portfolio replaced the old practical training logbook. And there was a new environmental health protection diploma for environmental health technicians.

The Housing Act 2004 finally brought in a form of licensing for the most dangerous houses in multiple occupation, as had been promised by Labour in two election manifestos. Integral to the legislation was the housing and health and safety rating system, a methodology for measuring and rating hazards that the CIEH had been responsible for developing through past president Stephen Battersby and EHP and legal expert David Ormandy.

The country was shocked in 2005 by a food safety tragedy. A wholesale butcher in South Wales who had misled EHOs with falsified records and failed to clean a vacuum packer properly caused an extensive outbreak of *E. coli 0157*. It was Wales' worst ever outbreak and the UK's second worst – 157 cases were identified, mostly children. Thirty-one victims were hospitalised. Tragically, one of them, five-year old Mason Jones, lost his life. Mason's mother, Sharon Mills, suffered her loss with braveness and dignity. She was to become a prominent food safety campaigner. Prof Hugh Pennington, who had chaired the inquiry into the Lanarkshire *E. coli* outbreak of 1996, performed the same task for the Welsh Assembly government. His report in 2006 stressed the importance of robust, professional and adequately-funded food safety inspection. Its recommendations led to a tightening up of food-safety procedures, particularly in Wales

As the 2005 election approached, the CIEH's policy team was busy. With pro-health charity Ash, it produced a Smoke Freedom Toolkit for local authorities. Policy officer Ian Gray was tasked with lobbbying MPs and other stakeholders around the country on the need for comprehensive smokefree legislation without exemptions. Widespread publicity was received for the CIEH's proposals for a 'Scores on Doors' scheme to grade food premises. The CIEH also highlighted the dangers of excessive UV radiation exposure from sunbeds, which had become a significant cause of skin malignant cancers, by means of a media campaign, a toolkit for local authorities and a national conference.

Julie Barratt, director of CIEH Wales, was particularly active and successful in this area, contributing to the UK's first sunbed safety legislation being introduced in Wales. She also worked hard to ensure that the environmental health profession was fully engaged with Wales' emerging public health agenda and produced a much-praised student training directory. In Northern Ireland, Gary McFarlane promoted the importance of environmental health and EHOs in the long-running NI review of public health and public administrations.

When New Labour won the general election of May 2005, the CIEH's groundwork paid off. The historic Health Act 2006 was judged by many to be the most significant piece of public health legislation since the Clean Air Act of 1956, fulfilling more than two decades of lobbying and campaigning from the

UK legislation passed in 2006 banning smoking from the workplace was a public health milestone

environmental health profession. The act prohibited smoking in all enclosed UK workplaces, including pubs, bars and restaurants. Wales and Northern Ireland went smokefree in April 2007 and England in July 2007. The Republic of Ireland had introduced smokefree laws in 2004. Opposition to the legislation, which had always been a minority pursuit backed by powerful vested interests, evaporated in the face of almost universal public acceptance.

Many EHPs had contributed to the introduction of this historic public health measure. As well as Ian Gray, who led on smokefree lobbying for the CIEH, the contributions should be noted of EHPs Maurice Mulcahy and Mike Garton. Mr Mulcahy carried out important research in the Republic of Ireland on the health damage to bar workers causes by passive smoking, widely disseminating his findings and campaigning for smokefree laws in the republic. In 2004, Mr Mulcahy's work was acknowledged when he received the CIEH's president's award.

In England, as CIEH policy officer with responsibility for health and safety, Mike Garton recognised that environmental tobacco smoke should be seen as a workplace health issue. Mike had been an officer in the Merchant Navy, principal EHO with Brighton Borough Council, then a popular consultant and trainer. He was awarded an MBE in 1997 and died tragically prematurely in 2005. He placed pressure on the Health and Safety Executive, which was initially resistant, to include the dangers of environmental tobacco pollution on its occupational health agenda.

In 2005, the CIEH joined with other public health organisations to co-found the Coalition for Public Health Action and Graham Jukes was appointed as an advisory board member on the NHS Public Health Leadership Programme. The year before, he had been awarded a fellowship by the Faculty of Public Health for his services to public health.

Concerned to streamline regulation, Gordon Brown had commissioned a report from Sir Philip Hampton, a former banker and chairman of Sainsbury's, when he was Tony Blair's Chancellor in 2004. Hampton's report led to the Regulatory Enforcement and Sanctions Act of 2008. It was to be one of the most significant features of Gordon Brown's three-year prime ministership, which began in 2007, when Tony Blair stood down.

The act gave a legal role to the Local Better Regulation Office to adjudicate disputes between businesses and regulators, issue guidance to local authorities and administer a new 'primary authority' scheme. This arrangement allowed food, health and safety and trading standards enforcement for multi-site businesses to be dealt with by a single body instead of multiple local authorities. It was slow to take off, but within five years, the scheme had captured the majority of the large high-street retail chains, including all the major supermarkets.

The LBRO, which was merged into the Department of Business Innovation and Skills in 2012 as the Better Regulation Delivery Office, was to provide a new focus for the environmental health profession. It highlighted synergies between EHPs and their colleagues, trading standards officers (TSOs), as regulators. From 2009, the CIEH came together with the Trading Standards Institute (TSI) and the LBRO in an annual Year Ahead conference held in February.

In 2006, the EU Registration, Evaluation, Authorisation and Restriction of Chemicals regulation was passed. Seven years in the making and governing the production of chemicals and their use in consumer products, it was the most complex legislation in the EU's history. Implementation was to be phased in over a decade.

The CIEH rounded off the last five years of the decade by re-organising its centres and branches so as to align with the government's regions. Each new region was asked to set up a management board and produce a business plan. The former commercial, independent and port health centres became special interest groups and a new international SIG joined them. Business plans were approved by the resources committee in 2007 and the new regions and SIGs were operational by January 2008.

On the professional front, as well as continuing to refine the degree and professional development, the CIEH, alongside colleagues in the TSI, worked to define professional competencies across a range of regulatory disciplines – health and safety, health protection and contaminated land, with food safety and housing to follow. Soon, EHPs would be able to map their competencies across agreed benchmarks and, if there were gaps, use an online resource to identify sources of help and training. The CIEH now had a London regional policy officer whose job was to promote environmental health in the capital, particularly to the mayor and assembly, assisted by Association of London Environmental Health Managers.

In 2007, the CIEH launched a new-style conference entitled The Best of the Best. In an era when professionals were busier than ever and budgets stretched, it was designed to be practical, affordable and participatory. Student numbers continued to increase. An associate parliamentary group on environmental health was established with the help of vice president Joan Walley MP. The group was designed to raise the profile of environmental health in the Houses of Commons and Lords.

The CIEH's state-of-the-art sustainable conference facility, 15Hatfields, has won plaudits and prizes

The following year, the CIEH opened 15Hatfields, a state-of-the-art conference and seminar facility that was managed sustainably and built, as far as possible, from recycled materials. One of its first major events was an international climate change conference. In a first for a CIEH event, the conference included live video links that were streamed on the CIEH website. Over the next five years, 15Hatfields would become a favourite venue of The Prince's Trust and attract an impressive roster of clients, including Orange and the Carbon Trust. In 2012, it was judged the UK's greenest conference facility by the food and farming charity Sustain.

A CIEH success in 2008 was the re-casting of part of the Planning Bill, awakening an interest in links between environmental health and planning. Around the same time, the poor management of the contaminated land regime was becoming increasingly acute. Created by MAFF and inherited by Defra, the regime aimed to bring former industrial or 'brownfield' land back into use, under Part IIA of the Environmental Protection Act 1990, particularly for new housing, of which there was a chronic shortage.

The need to protect health in that process lost focus with the transfer of responsibility to a part of Defra concerned with soil qaulity. The CIEH had established a standing conference on land contamination in 2003. But the cancellation of vital and overdue technical guidance gradually turned it from an ally into a critic of the department.

David Cameron and Nick Clegg formed a Conservative/Lib Dem coalition in 2010

When a general election was held in August 2010, the UK was plunging into a recession caused by an international banking crisis (the worst since the 1930s). Gordon Brown did not have a large enough majority to form a government and could not reach an agreement with the Liberal Democrat party.

Somewhat unexpectedly, an alliance formed between the Conservatives and the Liberal Democrats, producing a coalition government, with Conservative David Cameron as Prime Minister and a Lib Dem, Nick Clegg, his deputy. Like the coalitions of the inter-war years, it was leading a country on a crisis economic footing. To reduce the national debt, the government imposed swingeing cuts of up to 20 per cent across Whitehall and the public sector. Although the CIEH was in a strong financial position, its trading arm, like all companies, faced tough times.

Promising to set local government free and to get rid of 'top down' targets, the government scrapped Regional Development Agencies (they were replaced by

Local Enterprise Partnerships), the Audit Commission, with its myriad best value performance indicators and the Infrastructure Planning Commission. Gordon Brown's drive for better regulation now morphed into de-regulation, a policy goal that was pursued aggressively.

All 'regulation' was now potentially unwelcome – even that protecting health and safety or giving disabled people long fought-for rights. The government set up a website inviting the public to nominate regulations (some were acts of parliament) to be scrapped, but the public was not particularly enthusiastic. The CIEH pointed out that businesses often welcomed being visited by EHPs and TSOs.

Initially, the government's approach to health-related lifestyle issues – poor diet, smoking and drinking – was voluntary and low-key. Its 'responsibility deals' with industry groups attracted criticism from, for example, the professional medical associations, and sometimes derision.

Later, in the face of a health crisis caused by rising obesity and excessive drinking, the government's approach hardened somewhat. It moved towards introducing clearer food labelling and, in England, following the lead of the Scottish government, minimum unit pricing for alcohol was at least discussed. Many public health issues requiring secondary rather than primary legislation now came under the responsibility of the devolved legislatures of Scotland, Wales and Northern Ireland. From now on, there would be no uniform map of public health. The UK's nations would move ahead on policy issues at different speeds.

The government's early legislative programme was dominated by two large pieces of legislation. The Localism Act 2012 gave residents powers to demand referenda from their councils and introduced new, less secure tenancies and raised rents for tenants in social housing. The Health and Social Care Act 2012 was a large-scale structural reform of the NHS (something that Mr Cameron had said before the election that he would not embark upon) applying to England.

This act was contentious and took two years to pass through parliament, as it was fought over line by line. Controversially, it abolished primary care trusts and gave commissioning budgets to a new NHS Commissioning Board and to clinical commissioning groups (CCGs) formed from consortia of GPs. Purchasing services from a variety of providers, CCGs were to be responsible for 80 per cent of the NHS's budget. In theory at least, they would have an incentive to reduce budgets for acute services by promoting community-based provision.

The sections of the Health and Social Care Act concerning public health had been generally supported by the major political parties. They seemed to be in line with recent white papers, which had focused on preventing ill health and reducing inequalities. Under the act, NHS spending on public health was transferred to other bodies. It proved hard to calclute how much was already being spent and then how to distribute the money between areas of the country, equitably and according to need. Most of the money would fund a new agency, Public Health England, which would assume the functions of the Health Protection Agency, and a further tranche – £5.5bn for the next two years – would go to local authorities, ring-fenced to provide public health services. Levelling inequalities in mortality and health between regions and sub-regions was a specific objective of the legislation. Those local authorities achieving the best results against national criteria would receive high-performance rewards.

To guide what services they would offer to CCGs, upper-tier and unitary authorities would set up health and wellbeing boards, which would commission joint strategic needs assessments of their localities. Historically, the act also transferred approximately 500 directors and deputy directors of public health from the NHS to local authorities, where they normally worked in small, strategic departments, reporting to the chief executive. For the directors, it was a return to their employers from before the 1970 Social Services Act. One could interpret this as public health 'coming back' to local government.

EHPs could potentially play a valuable role in the new public health service, because of their subject knowledge, their links to other services and their skills in getting things done. However, times had changed. For one thing, it was clear that a multiplicity of local government services impacted on public health and wellbeing, including social care, planning, housing, economic development, parks, libraries and leisure facilities

The CIEH had responded to the government's public health white paper in 2011, supporting the government's desire to create a 'wellness' service and to strengthen national and local leadership. In recent years, it had played a leading role in the creation of the UK Public Health Register, providing a qualification route for professionals from non-medical backgrounds into public health leadership roles at consultant level – an opportunity that had been created by Sir Kenneth Calman, chief medical officer, in the 1990s. By 2008, 10 EHPs had achieved registration. In 2009, the first EHP from the register had become a director of public health in a joint local authority/NHS appointment – a milestone opening up a new horizon for the profession.

In the summer of 2009, was a disturbing *E. coli 0157* outbreak linked to a farm visited by children in Godstone, Surrey. It affected 93 people, including 76 children,

Godstone Farm in Surrey closed off after an outbreak of *E. coli 0157* that affected 93 people

some of whom suffered severe kidney damage, and it led to tighter precautions on 'petting farms'. The country may have been mired in financial gloom, but 2011 was the year of a Royal Wedding. In April, Prince William and Kate Middleton were cheered by 500,000 well-wishers as they married in Westminster Abbey. The coronation of 1953 had attracted a television audience of 20 million. This year's royal event was watched by two billion people around the world.

In 2012, the CIEH appointed its 29th president – the first woman to hold the role. Janet Russell was a former member of the General Council and had been a senior council director in Kirklees, helping to make it into a greener local authority. The CIEH looked forward, with keen anticipation, to the beginning of the new public health arrangements the following year. In November, it welcomed the new public health minister, Anna Soubry, to its award-winning venue, 15Hatfields, for a national conference.

In 2012, also, the CIEH awarded the title of Parliamentarian of the Year to Jeff Rooker, who was about to stand down as chair of the Food Standards Agency. The agency had had a generally successful 12 years. It had survived two quango culls, although in the second, it had lost its food education and advice role to the Department of Health. The agency's five-tier, food hygiene rating scheme had been almost universally adopted by English and Welsh local authorities (a form of 'Scores on the Doors' facilitating consumer choice), although display by business was not mandatory. In 2012, a new chief executive was appointed, Catherine Brown, former head of Defra's animal health and veterinary laboratories.

The CIEH now had 10,000 members working in all sectors (double its membership in 1952). More than 2,000 members had been awarded chartered status. It had a turnover of £10.8m and a staff complement of 111, based at Chadwick Court. The CIEH's suite of accredited qualifications had widened enormously, adding new topics like fire safety, first aid and environmental management. As an awarding body, the CIEH was accredited by the Qualification and Curriculum Authority and operated under the auspices of the Office of Qualification. The CIEH owned the majority stake in a profitable US subsidiary Environmental Health Testing LLC. This provided a food safety certification programme and was accredited by the American National Standards Institute. From small beginnings in the 1970s, it had become the world's leading examination body in food testing and training.

In 2012, the CIEH welcomed its first corporate member – InterContinental Hotels Group, the largest hotel provider in the world – and opened an office in Dubai, which joined Cardiff, Belfast and Orlando. It was now able to offer bespoke, accredited qualifications for companies and could deliver its qualifications by e-learning and other new routes. As a professional body, it had also expanded, fulfilling a growing demand for the skills of EHPs across the world. Twenty-two universities in six countries were accredited by the CIEH to offer BSc and masters degrees.

The CIEH's communication with members was sophisticated. It was now augmented by a secure intranet service, email communications and central and regional websites. There was a professional, peer-reviewed journal, *JEHR*. *EHN* as a magazine was now complemented by an editorial website, a weekly email newsletter, *EHN Extra*, a jobs website and email job alerts. In 2012, its editor, William Hatchett, won the Professional Publishers Association's independent publisher editor of the year award and art editor, Jon Heal, was shortlisted for designer of the year. Begun on a kitchen table, *EHN*, too, had come a long way.

Of course, 2012 was another landmark – it was the year of the Queen's Diamond Jubilee. For the most part, members of the CIEH had been unseen – keeping food wholesome, addressing poor housing and trying to protect the public from injury at work, nuisance and pollution. But, as we have shown, many played significant personal roles in the triumphs and tragedies of the Queen's remarkable reign. This book is designed to serve as a souvenir and illustrated record of the past 60 years. It is respectfully offered as such to Her Majesty.

Living with uncertainty

Geoffrey Podger played a vital role in environnmental and public health in the 2000s, heading up strategic regulatory bodies, tasked with protecting public safety. He was the first director of the new-look Food Standards Agency which emerged in 2000 from the ruins of the BSE crisis. Two years, later, in an EU newly-sensitised to cross-border food scares, he carried his UK experience abroad to head up a newly-established European Food Safety Authority. It was based in Palma in southern Italy.

In 2005, Mr Podger came back to the UK to be chief executive of the Health and Safety Executive, leading it through an era of stringent budget cuts, in a climate of deregulation. Like other parts of the Civil Service and the machinery of government, the HSE was migrated by New Labour – horror of horrors – to the frozen and unknown world north of Potters Bar.

In 2008 it relocated, controversially, from London to a single headquarters in Bootle on Merseyside. Under Mr Podger, the HSE moved from the number-of-inspections approach of the 'Revitalising health and safety' strategy launched by John Prescott in 2000 and, effectively, abandoned five years later, to a more nuanced strategy based on education campaigns targetted at occupational sectors and influencing behaviour. Whatever his critics said – the move to Bootle did not make him popular – Britain became a safer place on Mr Podger's watch, at least in terms of the measure of the number of people killed and seriously injured at work.

When he left the HSE in 2013, he had spent 16 years at the most senior levels in food and health and safety regulation. Always affable and formulating his thoughts in elegant phrases (a mandarin's mandarin) Mr Podger now enjoyed a unique vantage point. He could review the political and cultural trends that had influenced an area of policy which is vital to health and wellbeing but never fashionable and whose practitioners too often attract opprobrium.

Mr Podger recalls: "My involvement in the regulatory world began when I took over as Head of Food Science in MAFF in the mid 1990s. My main observations were the very high quality of the staff and the work that was being done but coupled sadly not merely with a lack of recognition but also a climate of positive distrust following the BSE crisis.

Geoffrey Podger civil service high-flyer who ran strategic food and safety bodies

"Getting that trust back required the creation of a new agency (the Food Standards Agency) which arrived with the new decade. It embodied a new approach of transparency and a readiness to engage with critics and commentators, which was unusual for that time. Public trust was regained in the food chain. Moreover, much to the irritation of Sir Humphrey-types in the Civil Service, various myths previously widely believed in government circles were exploded.

"Principal amongst these misconceptions was the view that the public could never accept that food could be other than 100 per cent safe, that any warning about any product deficiency would lead to immediate public panic and - perhaps most entertainingly - that everyone believed everything they read in the newspapers, however far-fetched. All these fallacies were very effectively disproved by the use of high-level spokespeople such as John Krebs and Susie Leather, chair and deputy chair of the FSA, effective communication and support from stakeholders.

"Moving to run the European Food Safety Authority, which I did in 2003, raised other challenges. First, the authority was, and remains, a body to provide scientific advice to the risk managers. This split of responsibility was always contentious not least as the risk managers seemed to believe that they would also have exclusive rights to communicate on risk which was clearly incompatible with the belief that EFSA should be a transparent agency. It also meant that tensions arose which could not easily be resolved between a seemingly politically-motivated risk manager anxious to meet popular prejudice (for example, on GMOs) and an agency that wished to produce science-based risk assessments without fear or favour.

"The early days of EFSA were certainly bedevilled by this kind of argument and in my view it is much to EFSA's credit that it refused to give in to those who shouted the loudest but did not have the evidence to back up their contentions. I think this remains its outstanding contribution to the EU.

"Returning to the UK to take up the reins at the Health and Safety Executive provided a contrasting experience to working in the food safety arena. The HSE had exactly the opposite problem to FSA/EFSA with regard to risk: namely little interest or pressure from those affected by even relatively significant risks. Workplace risks are regarded much less as matters of concern than food safety is, even if, on any objective basis, the opposite should be true. In contrast to the FSA and EFSA, the HSE therefore found itself more likely to be involved in technical debates with other experts than in public debate.

"Moreover, the HSE found its efforts to get people to assess and act on real workplace risks constantly undermined by those who invoked health and safety erroneously to ban everything from cheese-rolling competitions to hanging baskets. Thus, oddly, much of the HSE's media effort has had to be focused not on issues of its concern but rather in disputing concerns raised by others.

"Whilst the organisations I have described posed different challenges, my experience of all of them has very much confirmed my belief in the value of public regulatory bodies. I may also say that, contrary to those who claim them to be filled with 'self-serving quangocrats', in my experience they tend to be staffed by talented and concerned staff who have put public service above the material rewards they could easily earn in the private sector.

"There will always be tensions between regulatory bodies and politicians. But with good will on both sides they are manageable and the outcome will be better than expert bodies under direct political control. Working in a regulatory environment has taught me that we underestimate the good sense of the public we serve. If you give people cogent and sensible advice they will act on it. Uncertainty is a condition of all our lives and people will accept it, if all that can reasonably be done to moderate potential risks has been done. Equally, people expect to be protected from serious and avoidable risks and as public servants we have to deliver for them. I hope I did."

The new landscape

Kate Harris, EHP, primary authority officer for Cherwell District Council and Oxfordshire County Council, writes: "After completing a BSc in environmental sciences in 1999, I took an MSc in environmental health at the University of Birmingham. I studied alongside some excellent EHPs. I completed training placements with Denbighshire County Council in North Wales, where I grew up, and with McDonald's in Salford and London.

"Having achieved EHRB registration in 2001, I left the UK for travel in sunnier climes. After a year, I landed back into Heathrow and did some short-term contract work for Westminster. Then I moved to Tower Hamlets, as a food safety EHP in the challenging and exciting Banglatown area. I loved every minute of my time at Tower Hamlets, and gained valuable experiences there.

"In 2005, I moved to Hackney, where I led on a number of projects, including the delivery of smokefree compliance. I worked closely with colleagues from the primary care trust, the Department of Health and local mental health services, I was also involved with a rare case of inhalation anthrax, working with the Health Protection Agency. Experiences in Hackney allowed me to complete the Assessment of Professional Development and to gain chartered status. In 2008, I moved to Islington as a principal EHP and began a masters in public health. I was delighted to win the CIEH president's award in 2011.

Illegal raves became a source of complaints and enforcement

"Next, I was appointed to the challenging role of primary authority officer for Sainsbury's, working for Oxfordshire and Cherwell councils. I continue to work privately for a number of organisations, including Healthworks in London and Festival Republic, and I was honoured to work as a volunteer EHP at the 2012 Olympic and Paralympic Games.

The career of new practitioner, Chris Cornish, also shows the job diversity and range of roles that an EHP could enjoy in the first decade of the 21st century. Chris converted to environmental health from the background of an environmental science degree taken at King's College and working in civil engineering.

In 2001, he became a technical officer with Suffolk Coastal DC and, like an earlier generation of pupil public health inspectors, was able to gain practical, hands-on work experience while studying for an environmental health degree at Middlesex University. His specialisms were contaminated land, noise, local air quality, drainage, waste and private water supplies.

He became an EHP in 2007. His duties at Suffolk Coastal now widened. He recalls: "I enjoyed forging working relationships with the police, community mental health teams, the Environment Agency and others. I was fortunate to be involved in varied and interesting cases including music festivals, nuclear power stations, weird and wonderful industrial noises, vulnerable adults and the colourful individuals that we inevitably come across from time to time.

"My most memorable case was accompanying three colleagues onto an illegal traveller site to seize a couple of van loads of speakers and associated equipment from a rave that was in progress. This was only made possible by four police public order units, police search teams, local police officers and a helicopter. A surreal moment in a Suffolk forest."

In 2011, Chris left Suffolk to become a consultant in environmental protection and acoustics. His work again involved a music festival – this time, advising the organiser on providing a safe water supply. He then moved to Malden DC, where he dealt with wind farm applications, private housing and food safety. He notes: "My career so far has been challenging and exciting. I have met fantastic people, many of whom are now friends."

Alastair Tomlinson was awarded the CIEH Ronald Williams Gold Award as the best environmental health student of 2000, the year that he graduated from the University of Wales Institute Cardiff. His career shows the divergence of public health policy in Wales from that in England and the role that EHPs can play in helping to shape national policy making.

He writes: "I began as an EHP in Cardiff Council's noise team, dealing with nuisance complaints, licensing and planning applications, but I also became involved with the Welsh branch of the UK Public Health Association. In 2003, I became the council's lead officer for investigating outbreaks of communicable disease. At the same time, I was helping to develop the council's position on public health and studying for a masters in Cardiff."

In 2005, he was seconded to work as a policy officer with the Welsh Local Government Association's health and wellbeing team. He led on the Welsh Local Government Association's preparations for the introduction of smokefree public places in Wales in 2007, advised the Welsh Government and gave radio and TV interviews on the subject. He comments: "One of the great advantages of devolution in Wales is that it becomes feasible for a civil servant to have a meaningful working relationship with representatives from all 22 local authorities. This certainly helps the free flow of information."

In 2008, he became a lecturer in environmental and public health at Cardiff Metropolitan University and, in 2012, presented a paper on environmental nuisance at the IFEH Environmental Health World Congress in Vilnius, Lithuania.

Food safety

David Statham, formerly head of Leicester's environmental health service and a CIEH trustee, was the Food Standards Agency's first director of enforcement. He recalls an eventful decade: "The FSA came into being in April 2000. It was seen by the newly-elected Labour government as the answer to the various food scares, including BSE, that had undermined confidence in UK food during the 1990s. Also, the then MAFF had the schizophrenic roles of both supporting and regulating the food industry.

"The agency was set up as a non-ministerial government department with a

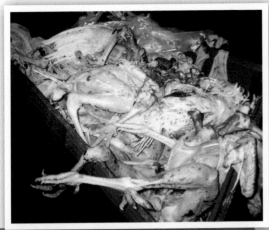

East Midlands EHOs closed down a pet food scam based in Denby, led by 'Maggot Pete'

huge amount of independence, reporting to a non-executive board. Working for the agency in those early days was exciting, as we sought to establish our independence and also our openness. Decision-making was the responsibility of the board at open meetings, during which members of the audience could ask questions and make statements.

"In 2000, we were in the middle of the BSE crisis and, as responsibility for BSE controls came under my watch, the issue took up a lot of my time. In November 2000, France reported its second case in an animal born after the feed ban. Since France had illegally banned British beef imports, there was a great deal of pressure on the UK to retaliate. Opposition MPs put pressure on the government to ban French beef.

"Against that background, on 29 November, 2000 I led a delegation to Paris to examine the French control system, so that the decision could be based on the best science rather than political rhetoric. We were followed all the way by a press caravan and, after the meeting, I made a statement to the media on the steps on a French ministry building. The agency made the decision to not ban French beef exports as the science didn't indicate that such action was proportionate and, in any event, it would have been illegal under EU law.

"If 2000 was about BSE, 2001 was dominated by foot and mouth. On 19 February, 2001, an observant meat inspector at Cheale abattoir in Essex detected the first case, which was later traced to a farm in Heddon-on-the-Wall. By the time the final all-clear was given in October, thousands of farm animals had been culled and incinerated on huge bonfires, which could be seen in rural areas all over the country.

"The outbreak was thought to be due to infected meat products. The finger of blame was pointed, to some extent, at controls operated by local port health authorities and pressure was brought to take controls away from local authorities and given to a national control body. But, thanks to collaborative working between the FSA and Port Health Authorities, confidence in imported food controls was restored.

"It is interesting that in 2012, issues concerning horse burgers and pork in halal food were prominent in the news, showing that what goes around comes around – or was it due to strict reductions imposed on the FSA and local authority budgets leading inevitably to fewer inspections and control measures?"

Dubious practices in the meat trade were again highlighted by EHOs in the new decade. In January 2001, following an investigation recalling Operation Meat Hook in the 1980s, three men were jailed for a total of 18 years for their roles in a diverted pet-food scam based in the East Midlands. They had trimmed rotten poultry meat and sold it to the catering trade through brokers.

The fraud had been detected in Rotherham, where three EHOs, led by Lewis Coates, were deployed in a full-time investigation, Operation Fox. The scam had been going on since the 1980s, netting the criminals millions. They were prosecuted for fraud, because of the inadequacy of sentences available under food law.

In the same year, a team from Amber Valley District Council led by a dedicated EHO, Sue Sonnex, detected another scam in which hundreds of tons of unfit, often putrid, chicken and turkey meat ended up in canteens and on supermarket shelves. This investigation was called Operation Aberdeen. The scam, based at a pet food plant in Denby in Derbyshire, was led by a man called Peter Roberts, nicknamed 'Maggot Pete'. In 2003, four of the perpetrators received prison sentences. 'Maggot Pete' had broken bail and fled to Cyprus but he was extradited back to the UK to begin his six-year sentence in 2007.

In London, Dr Yunes Teinaz was an EHO heavily involved in suppressing meat crimes. His targets included bush meat, sold in ethnic food markets; unfit 'halal' carcasses, often emaciated and transported warm and illegally slaughtered; and unskinned, smoked sheep, known as 'smokies'.

He recalls: "Many nights were spent following suspect vans or receiving telephone intelligence and passing on information on 'dirty meat' to EHOs all over the country." At that time, Dr Teinaz had a 'price' of £100,000 on his head.

Concerned about the prevalence of meat crimes, *EHN* magazine launched a Stamp it Out campaign in 2003. In the wake of Stamp it Out and the Rotherham and Denby cases, the FSA set up a national food-fraud advisory unit to help local authorities investigate and bring prosecutions in cases of organised crime crossing local authority boundaries.

London 2012

In 2012, the year of the Queen's Diamond Jubilee, the London Olympic and Paralympic Games put the capital city on the world stage. CIEH principal policy officer, Jenny Morris, was seconded to JLARS, a regulatory partnership of east London councils that covered the Olympic Park, and then into the Olympic organising committee, LOCOG, to manage food safety across all of the Olympic venues.

The CIEH's strategic projects director, Sharon Smith, was also heavily involved in the complex preparations for the games – the world's largest public event of 2012, attracting the attention of the world's media.

Whether helping to formulate a food policy or ensuring safe catering services and water supplies, both professionals were integral to the huge effort that made the games run smoothly. For the event itself, the CIEH supervised a team of 140 environmental health volunteers, including students, retired members and practitioners.

Wayne Blything, regulatory services officer with Ealing Council's noise and nuisance department, joined the team of volunteers organised by the CIEH for London 2012. Like many EHPs, he came to environmental health late from another occupational background – in Wayne's case, the sweaty world of restaurant kitchens.

He writes: "After 10 years of hard work and low pay, I decided on a change. I graduated in environmental health in July 2011. Initially, I was unable to find a placement with a local authority but I was fortunate to be offered a three-month placement with the CIEH in London, from January 2012.

Wayne Blything, chef turned EHO, samples water at the Olympic park

"Working at the CIEH's HQ at 15 Hatfields on London's South Bank, was the best thing that could have happened to me – it really opened up my eyes to how important our profession is, and, as well as exposing my lack of experience and knowledge, it gave me a hunger to succeed in my new profession.

"The CIEH placed me with the regulatory team, JLARS, for London 2012. My role varied. I might be helping with food safety inspections, deciding on swab points for bacteria testing kits, collecting water samples for the Health Protection Agency or accrediting volunteers. I felt privileged to part of a group that had such enormous responsibility for public health, ensuring the safety of hundreds of thousands of people. It reinforced just how important the work we do is, although it is out of the public eye and often unappreciated.

"After this, I worked as an EHP in Barking and Dagenham and Ealing. Like many EHPs, I work in partnership with antisocial behaviour teams, the police, adult and children's health services, social services and many other organisations. My first year as a graduate taught me a lot and my involvement with London 2012 was great. I can't wait to see what the future holds, especially when the new public health arrangements are in place."

Deathtrap housing

S tephen Battersby, past CIEH president, writes: "Throughout the 1980s and 1990s, there had been campaigns for the licensing of the private rented sector and particularly for properties converted into bedsits, or houses in multiple occupation. The Labour government came to power in 1997 with HMO licensing as a manifesto commitment and HMO licensing was brought in with the Housing Act 2004. But the scheme introduced was different from what had been campaigned for – national licensing applied only to HMOs of three storeys or more and with five or more occupiers. For many, the licensing regime and the definition of an HMO set out in the legislation seemed unnecessarily complex. Worse, there was no requirement to inspect an HMO before granting a licence.

"The 2004 Act, which came into force in 2006, did provide powers to local authorities to extend licensing to other HMOs beyond the mandatory criteria and also, in the form of selective licensing, to all private rented accommodation (not just HMOs) in a given area. The act also introduced a range of management orders, including interim management orders and empty dwelling management orders. EDMOs were designed to bring empty properties back into use when persuasion had failed but, in practice, were little-used.

"Part 1 of the act introduced a new methodology for assessing risk: the housing health and safety rating system (HHSRS). The system had been developed after almost a decade of research, following the dropping of the fitness standard in 1989. Initially, the HHSRS met with some resistance from the environmental health profession, which regretted the loss of the former fitness criteria. It was designed to be applicable to any form of residential accommodation.

"Another important change was that the new Residential Property Tribunal became the place to hear appeals under the act. This was an attempt to speed up decisions, providing an alternative to the courts. A number of EHPs sit on the RPT and the approach allows practitioners to deal with appeals themselves, without the need of a legal practitioner.

"The years after 2000 were also marked by a growth in the private rented sector, particularly in the form of buy-to-let housing, much of which was created speculatively and remained un-let. At the end of the decade the UK property market stagnated as the economy hit the doldrums. House-building in all sectors was at a low level. Waiting lists were lengthening, reflecting a huge unmet need for social housing, now provided by councils and housing associations. Tenants who were privately renting were far more likely to live in unhealthy or unsafe housing than those in any other sector.

"Local housing authorities could discharge their homelessness duty using the private rented sector, without the agreement of the applicant. There was a consensus that housing was in crisis – increasingly unaffordable and, for the most vulnerable, offering insecurity, poor conditions and, frequently, overcrowding. The CIEH joined other concerned organisations to form a lobby group – the Pro-Housing Alliance."

Environmental protection

The science of how chemical toxins affect those immediately in contact and future generations has become more sophisticated and has many branches. The health focus over the past couple of decades has not been on smokestacks bellowing dark plumes (largely a thing of the past) but on less visible agencies, such as persistent organic pollutants, heavy metals, nitrates and phosphates, with a focus on removing those that linger in land, air and water, and on mitigating the effects of new sources – including waste incineration, landfill and road traffic.

A class action was won by residents of Corby over negligence in cleaning up a steelworks

The landmark Environmental Protection Act 1990 consolidated UK law and harmonised it with that of the EU. One of its afterthoughts was a contaminated land regime, usually tasked to environmental health services, designed to facilitate the cleaning up the legacy of 19th and 20th-century pollution. In the meantime, new and potential hazards had appeared that 19th-century sanitary inspectors would not have dreamed of, including ionising and electromagnetic radiation, noise, light and nanomaterials.

In a new development, EHPs now advised residents claiming health effects, including birth defects, from disposed-of waste. In the Nantygwyddon landfill enquiry in 2001 and the Corby steel works case 10 years later, EHPs David Purchon and Roger Braithwaite took a prominent role as experts. Ruling on Corby, a judge found that the actions of Corby Council had exposed residents to potentially birth-defect causing chemicals, leading to an out-of-court settlement for damages.

Allegations of 'clusters' of ill health caused by pollution can lead to intense scientific and legal debate, often in court. But whatever the courts decide, their possible existence causes huge anxiety. In Northwich, Cheshire, the deaths of two young girls in 2004 and 2005 from acute myeloid leukaemia led to a public health investigation in a local community, recalls Rupert Adams.

He notes: "The multi-disciplinary incident team was aware of community concerns, particularly when it was discovered that their houses had been built on an old landfill in the mid-90s. We set out to discover what was known about AML, the local epidemiology and health, the landfill, and anything else that appeared relevant, to establish whether living on the estate was safe."

He adds: "From a starting point of suspicion and mild hostility towards the agencies, the incident team developed good relationships with the local community, involving them in the epidemiological studies and environmental surveys."

No potential cause of AML was found. The main risks in the housing were explosion from methane or asphyxiation from carbon dioxide arising from the landfill. "The council determined the land as contaminated and the social landlord undertook remediation works, placing gas membranes under ground floors, improving ventilation systems and disposing of contaminated soil."

A sustainable president

As CIEH president in 2002, Brian Hanna, formerly chief executive of Belfast City Council, made sustainability a theme of his term of office. Mr Hanna had been one of the group producing the CIEH's manifesto, *Agendas for Change*, and had been appointed to the government's Sustainable Development Commission, chaired by Jonathon Porritt. The commission was abolished by the coalition in 2011, reflecting a reducing government commitment to green politics, as the UK's economic position worsened.

Mr Hanna recalls: "When I retired from my position of chief executive at Belfast, I immediately took up the reins as president of the CIEH. It was a wonderful experience, which contained many memorable moments. These included visiting centres and branches throughout the UK and meeting and making many friends. Other highlights were attending the International Federation of Environmental Health conferences that were held in San Diego and Durban. I was visiting South Africa at a time when that country, like my own, was attempting to emerge from years of conflict and political stagnation. It was a fascinating experience.

"During my presidency, the CIEH annual conference was held in Belfast for the first time, and I chaired a president's commission, which was set up to investigate how the environmental health profession could rise to the great and wide-ranging changes that had taken place in local government over the previous 20 years. The Hanna report was the outcome of this work and I regard it as a useful contribution to the debate at that time.

"Environmental health never leaves you and in the 10 years since my retirement I have engaged in it in a variety of ways, such as working in the University of Ulster's School of the Built Environment as the Royal Academy of Engineering's sustainable development visiting professor and acting as deputy chairman of the Northern Ireland Science Park Foundation, a not-for-profit business support initiative located in Belfast's Titanic Quarter.

"I like to keep really busy. I'm also chair of Dublin Institute of Technology's recently-established Environmental Health Sciences Institute (EHSI), a research-based body involving the Ulster University funded by the Republic of Ireland's Government. In addition, I continue to represent the interests of CIEH as one of its vice presidents."

Port health

Long-distance flights had become dramatically cheaper from the 1990s, with the growth of budget airlines. The effect was to shrink the world and to increase the danger of the spread of human and animal diseases, including one, a new form of avian flu, which it was feared could cause a global pandemic, potentially killing millions of people.

On the sea, like body builders pumped up with steroids, passenger ships and ferries became dramatically larger. As chief port health inspector

Budget flights and container ports have revolutionised port health authorities

of the Hull and Goole Port Health Authority, Roy Kaye observed the trend of larger ships and more passengers coming through his port at first hand. The trend culminated in 2000 with the arrival of the *Pride of Hull* and *Pride of Rotterdam* ferries in Hull. They carried almost a million passengers a year and served three meals a day in restaurants and cafeterias.

He notes: "While the shipping line owners, P&O North Sea Ferries, were only too keen to co-operate fully with food hygiene requirements, the law regarding this was surprisingly vague. All that was available was a section of the Public Health (Ships) Regulations 1979 stipulating that conditions should not exist on board that could facilitate the spread of infectious disease. There were no applicable food hygiene regulations and no basic right of access to the ships to inspect them for food hygiene purposes."

He continues: "Unfortunately, there had been some infrequent cases of salmonella food poisoning on board ferries at Hull, which were fully investigated by our specialist port health team. On other cruise ferries at this time, illnesses such as winter vomiting disease, or Norwalk virus, were becoming more frequent – ships' passengers were prone to being infected by cross-contamination due to their close contact with other passengers during the voyage.

"It was decided to assign a port health inspector to be responsible for ferries and he or she would make an inspection voyage to either Rotterdam or Zeebrugge at least once a year to observe procedures and standards during overnight voyages. Temperature checks and bacteriological samples were taken and a comprehensive report presented to the ferry company following the journey. In addition, all the catering crew members attended the CIEH basic food hygiene course using interpreters. Also, the ships were awarded Heartbeat Awards."

Hull and Goole's deputy chief port health inspector, Geoffrey Lister, took a lead role in promoting food hygiene on the ferries. Mr Kaye notes: "The food hygiene courses, together with our in-depth inspections, were undoubtedly a key element in raising standards and awareness. Mr Lister presented a paper at the APHA conference in June 1993, presenting a case for applying food hygiene regulation to ferries. These initiatives were successful. In 2003, the Food Hygiene (Ships and Aircraft) Order made food hygiene regulations applicable on ships and aircraft visiting the UK."

Following the passing of the WHO International Health Regulations in 2005, there was a major shift in the way ships were inspected. Ship sanitation certificates are now issued in authorised ports, valid for six months, and ship inspection has broadened to include all sanitation issues and risks, including food safety and ID controls.

Licensing

Local authorities took on an important new responsibility in 2005. For years, liquor licensing had been administered by magistrates. Magistrates also dealt with music and dancing licences until 1983, when councils assumed responsibility for public entertainment licensing. In 2005, the Licensing Act of 2003 passed responsibility for liquor licensing to councils and made licensing hours more flexible.

DR Krieger of Southend-on-Sea recalls: "The safety and licensing team faced its biggest administrative challenge, with new, complex and untested legislation to administer. Coupled with that, we had a special cumulative impact policy in the town centre, which presented great potential for challenge in the High Court. We had a tight timescale, with more than 600 premises licences and 900 personal licences to grant by the end of November.

Responsibility for managing liquor licensing was passed from magistrates to local authorities

"But we had assembled an excellent team of officers, who brought their own skills, experience and abilities to the job. Our tasks included mastering the detailed regulations, statutory guidance and 'embedded rights' carried over from the Licensing Act 1964, and ensuring that the council's licensing committee was fully trained and equipped. We also had to help applicants or their lawyers with the complexities of the new law and help local residents understand their rights in relation to licence applications that might affect them. We were anxious to meet or, if possible exceed, the high standards achieved by the courts, which had established an excellent reputation for their fairness.

"As the trickle of early applications turned into a torrent, we scrambled into action, commandeering the meeting room as our 'Bomber Command', with stacks of files six feet high surrounding the door, like sandbags and with marker boards pressed into service to plot our course. But, with dedication and hard work, we succeeded. It truly was team spirit at its best, with officers working late into the evening and at weekends, to meet deadlines for preparing reports, convening hearings and issuing licence documents.

"Our success earned us the respect of elected members, our professional peers, our partners in the licensed trade and the legal profession. We were at pains to ensure that the new licensing authority was recognised from the outset for its high standards. This has been proved by an exceptionally low level of appeals against the authority's decisions. The next phase was implementation. In the licensed trade, competition is fierce so that if one venue gains some advantage, such as extra hours, their business rivals seek the same. This has led to a continued round of applications for new or varied licences, sometimes involving strongly contested three-day hearings."

Following this successful transfer, the government passed the Gambling Act in 2005. This legislation transferred licensing responsibilities for casinos, betting shops, bingo halls and amusement arcades from magistrates to councils.

Public health

Formed in 2012, ready to assume its statutory functions the following year, a new body, Public Health England, was given a bold overarching purpose. Reflecting the coalition government's stated aim of levelling differences in life expectancy, the new executive agency of the Department of Health was tasked "to protect and improve the nation's health and wellbeing, and to reduce health inequalities".

Coming in an era in which quangos were more typically being merged or abolished, it was a relatively large creation. PHE was given a £485m budget and allocated 5,000 staff, 4,000 of whom were scientists. It took over several nationally-important establishments, including the Porton Down laboratories, the UK centre for emergency preparedness for a radiological or nuclear attack, and Colindale, the infectious disease centre.

The agency took over the functions of the former Health Protection Agency to run England's protection systems for infectious disease, microbiological hazards and environmental emergencies. Secondly, its role was to co-ordinate the new public health function of local government. PHE's first chief executive, Duncan Selbie, was a career NHS manager, who had left school at 15 to work as a clerical officer for Tayside Health Board and risen through the ranks.

Assisted by a senior leadership team and an executive board, Mr Selbie reported, like the chief medical officer, Sally Davies, to the health secretary. Talking to the CIEH's magazine, *EHN*, Mr Selbie said that he regarded EHOs as a vital part of the local government public health workforce.

On the ground, local authorities prepared to take on new responsibilities at the same time as reeling under swingeing cuts imposed by the coalition government, following the banking collapse of 2008. Many environmental health services were freezing appointments or cutting staff. Some services merged. In November, 2012 one authority, North Tyneside, was the first to outsource its environmental health and trading standards functions to a company, Capita Symonds.

But some in the environmental health profession working in local government, saw opportunities rather than threats on the horizon in the beginning of a new era. Chris Allen, public protection services manager with West Lindsey DC, comments: "In the Queen's Diamond Jubilee year, 2012, environmental health was at a crossroads, anticipating the arrival of ring-fenced public health funding. At a time when their budgets were under sever pressure from centrally-imposed cuts, councils were at the threshold of the most exciting opportunity in public health that I had experienced in my 22 years working in a local authority public health arena.

"While public health funds may only be ring-fenced in the short-term, I still believe that, as councils providing public health services, we have been gifted a unique opportunity from the reforms. There are significant reasons to welcome the reforms. Firstly, amidst, or because of, a time of great change in the NHS, our stakeholders have never been more receptive to the development of alliances and partnerships that can help them to deliver improved health outcomes. Councils and their health partners should be able to re-focus their efforts to meeting local needs instead of what matters to central government.

"Never can I remember a more profound opportunity in which such a large range of major health organisations have embarked upon the same journey. As practitioners, my view is that we should not rely on luck and national circumstances but redouble our efforts, foster alliances and develop a collaborative approach. I am confident that the conclusion will be better health and wellbeing for our residents."

Duncan Selbie, PHE, and Graham Jukes, CIEH, sign a partnership agreement

In 2013, as the profession embraced its new public health role, an historic partnership agreement between CIEH and Public Health England was signed. In November of that year, a five-year financial strategy and corporate plan was agreed, designed to accelerate the growth of the CIEH and to allow significant investment in the profession at home and abroad.

To match the rapidly changing landscape affecting the CIEH and its members, new governance arrangements were implemented in order to streamline decision-making – including a slimmed-down, 10-person board of trustees, chaired by Andy Statham, and a commercial board, chaired by Geoff Ward.

As he approached his 25th year working for the CIEH, chief executive Graham Jukes was awarded an OBE in the 2014 New Year Honours list. He comments: "It was a great honour which I accepted on behalf of the many people who had supported the work I had done during a period of great change in the profession."

He adds: "I am confident that the CIEH is well-placed to continue its work as we head towards a general election in 2015, with important debates being conducted about Europe, devolution, growing health inequalities, poor housing, food safety and climate change.

"The original timeframe for this book ended in 2012, but time marches on. I will leave it to others to chart the history of the profession over the coming years, confident that it is well-equipped to continue its historic mission of putting wrong things right."

Chronology 2000-12

2000

■ Health Development Agency replaces Health Education Authority.

■ Food Standards Agency begins. European food safety white paper. Licensing of English butcher shops.

■ Local Government Act establishes mayors and cabinets. Urban white paper.

■ Phillips report into BSE crisis.

■ Fuel shortages and protests.

■ Contaminated land regime begins. Revitalising health and safety strategy.

■ Regulation of Investigatory Powers Act. places controls on 'covert surveillance'.

2001

February Foot and mouth outbreak.

11 September terrorist attack in New York.

■ Labour wins second election victory. MAFF replaced by Department for Environment, Food and Rural Affairs (Defra).

■ Primary care trusts and strategic health authorities begin.

2002

■ Golden Jubilee of Elizabeth II.

■ Wanless Report recommends more spending on preventive services.

■ CIEH publishes *Environmental Health 2012* setting a 10-year strategic vision.

■ European Food Safety Authority begins .

■ *Journal of Environmental Health Research* (JEHR) launched.

2003

■ Denby meat fraud trial. Four men jailed. *EHN* launches Stamp it Out campaign.

■ Health Protection Agency begins.

■ Licensing Act transfers liquor licensing from magistrates to local authorities.

■ Chartered status for CIEH members.

■ Food Hygiene (Ships and Aircraft) Order applies food hygiene regulations to ships and aircraft.

2004

■ Irish smoking ban.

■ Tsunami in south-east Asia kills more than 275,000 people.

■ New EU food safety regulations.

■ Accredited Associate grade of CIEH membership introduced.

■ North-East votes no to an elected regional assembly, killing plans for English devolution.

2005

May Election returns Tony Blair to power.

7 July bombing in London kills 56 people.

- Buncefield fuel depot explosion.

- South Wales *E. coli* outbreak.

- Hampton Report into regulation. Health Development Agency abolished.

- Gambling Act. Transfers powers to local authorities.

2006

NO SMOKING.
It is against the law to smoke in these premises

- Health Act 2006. Legislation restricting smoking in England, Wales and Northern Ireland.

- Housing Act 2004. Licensing of bedsits and housing health and safety rating system.

- 2004 EU Food Safety Regulations strengthens requirement for hazard analysis in food premises.

- 1,000th chartered EHP announced.

2007

- Gordon Brown becomes Prime Minister.

- New corporate manslaughter offence.

2008

- CIEH opens 15Hatfields and hosts national climate change conference.

- Regulatory Enforcement and Sanctions Act. Local Better Regulation Office and primary authority system begin.

2009

- UK enters recession.

- Fire at Lakanal House in Camberwell, a council high-rise block, kills six people.

- High Court rules against Corby Council in birth defect case.

- Pennington report into the 2005 S. Wales *E. coli* outbreak.

2010

May Coalition government forms, led by David Cameron.

- Largest public sector spending cuts for 50 years.

- CIEH announces InterContinental Hotels Group as its first corporate member.

2011

- Fukushima nuclear plant disaster in Japan.

- CIEH opens office in Dubai.

- Localism Act reduces security of tenure and raises council rents.

2012

- Janet Russell becomes first female CIEH president since its incorporation in 1883.

- Health and Social Care Act transfers ring-fenced public health funding to local authorities and Public Health England.

- Celebration of Diamond Jubilee of HRH Queen Elizabeth II and London 2012 Olympic and Paralympic Games.

Appendix one

The profession's name changes

1872-1957 ....Sanitary Inspector
1957-1975 ....Public Health Inspector
1975- ....Environmental Health Officer

CIEH name changes

1883......................Association of Public Sanitary Inspectors
1891......................Sanitary Inspectors' Association
1957......................Association of Public Health Inspectors (APHI)
                (coat of arms acquired)
1975......................Environmental Health Officers Association (EHOA)
1981......................Institution of Environmental Health Officers (IEHO
1994- ....Chartered Institute of Environmental Health (CIEH)

CIEH journal name changes

1895......................*The Sanitary Inspector's Journal*
1902......................*The Sanitary Journal*
1932......................*The Sanitarian*
1964......................*The Public Health Inspector*
1968......................*Environmental Health*
1998......................*Environmental Health Journal*
2005......................*Environmental Health Practitioner*
2011- ....*Environmental Health News*

Appendix two

Presidents since 1952

1952-1956	Lord Milner of Leeds
1956-1957	Sir Ivor Jennings
1957-1960	Lord Bossom of Maidstone
1960-1963	Rt Hon James Griffiths MP
1963-1966	Arthur Blenkinsop
1966-1967	Robert Mathew MP
1967-1970	John Graham OBE
1970-1971	Eldon Griffiths MP
1971-1974	E.M. Birtwistle
1974-1976	John Marriott
1977-1979	E.N. Wakelin OBE
1980-1983	A. Archer MBE
1984-1986	Roy Emerson
1987-1990	Eric Foskett OBE
1991-1993	John Tiffney MBE
1993-1996	Andrew Banfield OBE
1996-1999	Alan Johnson
1999-2001	David Purchon
2002-2004	Brian Hanna CBE
2004-2007	Alan Higgins
2008-2011	Dr Stephen Battersby
2012-	Janet Russell OBE

Council Chairmen since 1952

1952	D. Powell MBE
1953	N. Bastable
1954	J. Graham OBE
1955	J. Marriott
1956	G. Rowe
1957	G. Saffin
1958	Major D.J.E Lamb
1959	E.M. Birtwistle
1960	R. Young
1961	A. Jump
1962	S.G. Fisher
1963	G.A. Hilller
1964	K.C. Benham
1965	A. Archer MBE

1966.....................E. Dodsworth
1967.....................H.C. Boswell
1968.....................N. F. Cripps
1969.....................W.Parker
1970.....................F.G.Caudrey
1971.....................T.H. Iddison MBE
1972.....................R.A. Hallet
1973.....................R.V. Redston
1974-1976............A.J.Stroud
1976.....................H.Herbert
1977.....................H.Corscadden
1978.....................R.Emerson
1979.....................Ian Eames
1980.....................Alan Kirkman
1981.....................John Greig
1982.....................Eric Foskett OBE
1983.....................D.E. Smith
1984.....................John Tiffney MBE
1985.....................Donald Barnett MBE
1986.....................Alan Johnson
1987.....................Terrence Brunt
1988 ....David Hornsey
1989.....................Andrew Banfield OBE
1990.....................Patricia Jefford
1991.....................John Kirk MBE
1992.....................Clifford Ride
1993.....................Brynley Jones
1994.....................Christopher Lingard
1995.....................David Statham
1996.....................Stephen Miller
1997.....................Graham Slee
1998.....................Peter Archer
1999.....................John McCandless
2000.....................Leslie Milne
2001.....................Stephen Young
2002.....................Clive Wadey
2003.....................John Bryson
2004.....................Timothy Deveaux
2005.....................Dr Stephen Battersby
2006.....................Siobhan Toland
2007 ....Janet Szlamp
2008.....................Mark Elliott

2009......................John Freear
2010......................Alan Higgins
2011......................Bob Foster
2012- ....Andrew Statham

Chief Executives since 1952

1950-1977 ....Reginald Johnson MBE (General Secretary)
1978-1986 ....Ken Tyler
1986-1990 ....Bob Tanner
1990-1994 ....Terry Brunt
1995-2000 ....Michael Cooke
2000- ....Graham Jukes OBE

CIEH Vice Presidents, 2012

Baroness Sally Hamwee
Dr June Crown
F.A. Osborne (Derek) CB
Joan Walley MP
John W Spence
Morris McAllister
Brian Hanna CBE
Professor Graham Ashworth CBE
Professor Hugh Pennington CBE
Professor Sir Kenneth Calman
Professor Tim Lang
Rt Hon Kevin Barron MP